NØ
TIME
TO
HATE

Lexius Henson's Journal of Enlightenment

CRAIG E. RUSH

Third Eye Pyramid
Westland, MI

NO TIME TO HATE: LEXIUS HENSON'S JOURNAL OF ENLIGHTENMENT

Third Eye Pyramid Publishing

Westland, MI

ISBN: 978-0-9861912-0-6

This is a work of non-fiction. Names and places were authenticated. Parts of this work came from spiritual intervention between Lexius Henson Sr. and the author. The content of this work is to be construed as the actual thoughts of Lexius Henson Sr. and the author.

First Edition November 2018

Cover Design by: Make Your Mark Publishing Solutions

Interior Design by: Make Your Mark Publishing Solutions

Editing by: Make Your Mark Publishing Solutions

Printed in the United States of America

NØ
TIME
TO
HATE

LEXIUS HENSON'S JOURNAL
OF ENLIGHTENMENT

To Mary E. Rush and Roy E. Rush, primarily instilling in me to have free thought. The sacrifices they made for my siblings and me are not to be weighed by any scale of gold. Mom, your legacy is etched in stone forever now, and I pray that it gives you eternal peace.

To the human race and Lexius Henson Sr., who used me as a vessel to purvey his dream of unifying all races and for us to unite and understand that we are all one.

Acknowledgments

Without my siblings being a part of this discovery, I could have never been inspired to write this book. Anthony, Denise, Nathaniel (who has passed before us, but I know he was there when I wrote this book), Joselynn, Karen, Kathy, Roy Jr., I want to thank you all for your dedication to this plight of giving our mother and ourselves some closure to our heritage. I love you all far greater than the definition of love. Uncle Roscoe, I can't leave you out, for without your fervor for family heritage and your insight, this book would not be possible.

Krystal Jackson, you get your own line, cousin. I know that Lexius Henson Sr. has used both of us to open the portal to our lineage. We have yet to meet in person, but I see you every day. Continue to do what you do, and we are far from the journey Lexius has placed upon us. It is our obligation to set his soul to rest.

Thank you, Shaniece. You know what you did for me. On that note, thank you, Brucey for your interest and research. Kathey, thank you so much because I know your passion for our family history is equal to mine, if not greater. I want to thank those who inspired me to complete this book. You know who you are. To Crecia and my offspring, Deja Lauren, Craig'Michael, and Diamond'Nicole, thank you for giving me space, even though you might not have understood the depth of my journey. Thanks, Chippy for keeping me motivated, and I know you are going to go on and write even greater works.

Gotcha, Robert Williams! You thought I'd forgotten you. You

will always leave an intelligible impression on my inspirations. I want to thank you, especially for our many early-morning calls about this book and your teachings of wisdom. They will not go unrewarded. Continue to keep your mindset, because it is on point and you have changed many lives for the better with your insight. We debated often, but you are the teacher of truth.

I want to thank everyone in the Rush clan for your continual support for your family. We always have thought-enriching conversation. Dare to make your dreams a reality. All is possible, regardless of the naysayers. A special thank you goes to my new family, the King clan. I can't wait to have a first meeting with you all. Our blood runs deep. There is a lot of rich heritage in our lineage and we must continue to discover it.

Thank you, Constance Turner and Uncle Raleigh Borum. Your regal demeanor is a personification of our rich heritage. And my beautiful Aunt Michelle, I still await our meeting. This is part of your story, and I am so glad to have had you come into our lives. We love you so much. Thanks, Harlan Eberhardt Jr. (Buffy) for late-night wisdom. Anthony Carter, keep reaching for the brass ring. To Thais, Mark, and Desiree, keep growing.

In Loving Memory

P.R. Pryor, thank you for who you were, your plight, and your strength.
Uncle Son - Hugh Henson
Grandmother Mattie Lee Henson Pryor
Gertrude Henson King
Hattie Pryor Henson
David King
Nathaniel Royce Webber
Lexius Henson Sr.
Roy E. Rush Sr.
Anthony F. Webber Sr.

INTRODUCTION

This work is a journal of enlightenment, inspired by Lexius Henson, Sr., an entrepreneur from pre and post-Civil War times and one of the most influential individuals of the era. He was one of the richest mulatto men in the South. Most probably would have never heard of him unless they'd done research on John Hope, the first black president of Atlanta University and Morehouse College. Lexius Henson Sr. employed John Hope from the age of twelve into adulthood. John went on to become a founding member of the Urban League and one of the most influential educators of the time. John was also of mulatto descent.

Lexius Henson was the owner of one of the finest restaurants in the country, Lexius Henson's Exchange Saloon and Restaurant in Augusta, Georgia. He had the finest china silverware and linens, designed with his monogram stamped or embroidered onto each elegant piece. Some of the most prominent people dined at his restaurant, generals on both sides of the Civil War, including Sherman and Lee. They say his food was so good that General Sherman's March to the Sea was originally mapped to go right through Augusta to the Atlantic Ocean; however, Sherman realized Lexius's restaurant would be destroyed and he would have no place to celebrate his great victory, so he changed course.

Lexius hosted governors, mayors, princes, Rockefeller, Carnegie, Fairchild, and Morgan. These great men often used Lexius's knowledge as they partook in his worldly and newly concocted delicacies. They imbibed the finest cognacs, whiskies, ales, and wines, and puffed cigars that were only made available to the elite. Some of the descendants of his prestigious guest list are the controlling forces of the modern era.

Lexius was a learned man, historian, and son of a prominent doctor from South Carolina. He was privy to the proverbial secrets of the world, of which he took full advantage to advance his wealth. His advice was honored as that of a modern-day psychologist and a Wall Street broker with the wealthiest portfolio.

This story shares his profound wisdom, the most important reason for this work. It details his dream: the unification of the human race. It entails the journey of a few men who changed the world for good and not so good. It is meant to challenge you to open your eyes and be a person, an individual, who, even if nobody knows your name, can make all the difference in the world.

Lexius's life was incorporated into the lives of many other people around him. He broadened minds, helped to expand ideals, and shaped the character of many; the depth of the benefits mankind received from his existence is unfathomable. No ink on paper can truly ascertain his importance.

He awakened thought in some of the most powerful men through his presence. He lessened or removed many prejudices about, not only, his race, but all races. He incited wisdom and knowledge in the minds of perplexed philanthropists and statesmen. Lexius's energy and worth were examples of accomplishment, stimuli to people of both the black and white races to better the quality of life and do good for others, even though some considered him to be a godless man, only concerned with self-worth.

I will not trouble those who read these lines with a lengthy historical exposition. This is the story of my great-great—and I do mean *great*—grandfather, Lexius Henson, Sr.

Enjoy! Turn on the light. Pay attention!

UBUNTU

An anthropologist proposed a game to the children of an African tribe. He put a basket of fruit near a tree and told the kids that the first one to reach the fruit would win them all. When he told them to run, they all took each other's hand and ran together; then they sat together, enjoying the fruit.

When asked why they ran like that, as one could have taken the fruit all for oneself, they responded, "Ubuntu! How can one of us be happy if all the others are sad?"

Ubuntu is a philosophy practiced by African tribes that is often translated as, "I am because we are."

"I have a cellar of knowledge of which I limit the amount I share because of the intoxicating effect it may have."

–C.E.R.

CHAPTER 1
REFLECTIONS OF MY SOUL

There I sat many a day, looking into the eyes of a portrait that was the reflection of my soul, a picture of a man of obvious means of his era. He had a very strong, austere stare, his wife standing, as if a statue, beside him, relaying the same story that was on his face. It was a portrait lacking any information of its history or its subject's bloodline. It was given to my mother by her uncle, Hugh Henson (Uncle Son). All my mother had told me was that he was my great-grandfather. I later found out through research for this book that he was actually my great-*great*-grandfather, Lexius Henson, Sr. My mother also revealed that he lived as a white man by day and a black man by night. Uncle Son and his sister, Mattie Lee, my mother's mother, were the products of a marriage between Lexius Henson, Jr. and Hattie. Hugh would later have to change his last name to Henderson after an exodus to the North to escape his past after he'd done something in the South that was forbidden by a man of his color. Uncle Son had almost beat a white man to death because the white man had called him an "uppity nigger." Uncle Son had tried to walk away, but the man continued to taunt him until Uncle Son just snapped.

NO TIME TO HATE

Yet, did I know that my champagne and caviar taste was fed to me through DNA. I had, and still have, a constant craving for higher learning and the finer things in life as a result, I believe, of my bloodline that I would later discover in writing this book. My mother would always tease me and say she'd brought home the wrong baby. She would say that my taste and fervor for life were beyond that of our comfortable upbringing. It goes back to the Assyrian belief that your outcome or the journey you choose is directly an inherent factor. My parents always had an air of royalty upon their presence. When my mother enters a room, she is the personification of regal upbringing. She still has a southern drawl to her speech, even though she has been in the North for over sixty years.

Many a night, I could feel my mother's anguish when she told me stories of her family heritage, what little she knew of it. It brought her joy or some form of relief as she spoke of her time growing up in Ward I in Augusta, Georgia. Mom only knew of four living relatives: Uncle Raleigh, Cousin Willie, Constance Turner, and her sole sibling, Michelle. Mom and Michelle had different fathers and their mother had died five months after giving birth to Michelle. Mom had lost touch with Michelle, who was twenty-one years her junior. Mom began her nursing training after they were separated and she moved to Nebraska, where she met her first husband during World War II, a Navy man named Athon. This union produced four children. They would eventually divorce but maintained a close relationship without malice. Mom then married a man named Roy and had four more children, including myself. I always lived with all my siblings. We all had a close relationship with Athon and his new family as well. Mom believed in closeness of family.

It would take forty years before my mother and her sister, Michelle, would reunite. None of us eight siblings had ever met our aunt, only seeing her in the one picture Mom had. One Christmas, my sister-in-law, Angie, the wife of my brother, Roy Jr., being of compassionate character, could no longer sit by and see the pain and void in Mom's life because of a lack of heritage. Angie asked my mom if she had a number or address for Michelle and asked why she had not attempted to contact her. Mom's eyes began to well up as she explained that many a letter had been written but went unanswered.

Mom and Angie are our house detectives and neither will stop until she is satisfied with her investigations. This was only one of two mysteries yet to be solved by my mom, so Angie couldn't understand why this connection hadn't occurred. For Mom, it was like being a doctor; you are your own worst patient. She could solve any mystery but her own.

After a family prayer, Angie said, "Ma, give me the number. Tonight, we are going to get a resolution." Mom had attempted to reach her sister on many occasions, but phone calls had gone unanswered. Letters sent during the holidays in hopes that Michelle would get them also went unanswered. Angie called the number and quickly explained her relationship. As a preacher's daughter, she appealed to Mrs. Johnson, the wife of a preacher, to help bring relief to our family. The conversation lasted five to ten minutes as I sat holding my mother, who was in tears, along with my other siblings, anticipating the outcome of the conversation.

Angie hung up the phone with an optimistic but confident look, a look I knew to be of determination. It meant that she was going to get to the bottom of this. We asked her to repeat every word that was said. Angie stated that Mrs. Johnson hadn't been defiant and she had appealed to her spiritualism to do the right thing. Mrs. Johnson had agreed and that was it. Angie could sell ice to an Eskimo, curse you out in her soothing Virginia accent without being vulgar, and have you thanking her when she's done. I could see some relief in Mom's eyes as she wiped away her tears. I thought to myself that this act alone would at least add some years to my mother's life and some hope that this Hollywood script-like situation would play out with a happy ending.

Five minutes later, the phone rang. We had gone back to our normal loud, jovial conversations and almost didn't hear the phone. Angie picked up the phone as if she knew who was on the other end, having never answered the phone at our parents' house in Cleveland before. All we heard was the usual, "Hi. How are you doing? Hold on please,"

and figured it was just a holiday call from a well-wisher. As Angie handed Mom the phone, she gave the group a look and, simultaneously, Mom screamed and burst into tears. Across the void and pain, Mom was listening to the voice of her lost sister, Michelle. It was the best Christmas ever.

This beautiful little girl, Michelle, hadn't a choice in the matter. She had been told throughout the years that her sister didn't want anything to do with her because of their different lineage. Mom was of mulatto descent: Her father was a white man and her mother's father was a white man. Michelle's father was of African America descent, but both were the beautiful fruit of a mulatto woman, Mattie Lee, who knew no distinction, only love. Michelle had been taken away by the other side of the family.

What could have occurred if these two sisters had never parted? What did occur was a void of forty years, wondering, and grief every day of Mom's life as she existed with my father's close-knit family and celebrated heritage. It gave her great despair. My mom is a strong, resilient woman, but also human. What was the effect on both beautiful creations, siblings sharing the same emptiness all because of the prejudices that existed within a few people who made the decision to create this forty-year saga? Those years can never be made up, but they continue to bond stronger each day.

My mom moved to the North via marriage to Athon Webber from Tennessee. The father of Mom's sister, Michelle, was married to their mother, my grandmother, Mattie. Mattie had a very rough childbirth with Michelle. I never had the privilege of meeting my grandmother, who died five months after giving birth to Michelle. Michelle's father, J.C. Bond, took custody of Michelle. He mysteriously died in a house fire when Michelle was two years old. His death was rumored to be foul play. Then came the custody battle between J.C. Bond's mother and her two aunts, Lorrene and Irene. Irene would prevail. She also won the inheritance. Lorrene would later take over custody after Irene passed. Lorrene is still alive and she is who my sister-in-law had contacted for Michelle and Mom's reunion more than forty years later.

Michelle and Mom didn't have the privilege of memories of their fathers. Mom, at least, was privy to time with her mother. I don't have much information about J.C. Bond, other than the fact that he was jet black and my mom did not take a liking to his personality or the way he treated her. Michelle's only memory of her mother was through pictures that Mom sent her. One was a picture of J.C. Bond with Mattie.

Michelle and Mom were the great-granddaughters of Lexius Henson Sr. and Mattie was the sister to Hugh Henson (known as Uncle Son), who would later change his name to Henderson after his exile from Georgia after nearly killing a white man.

Lexius Henson Sr. and his brother Charles were the sons of a prominent doctor from South Carolina. They migrated to Augusta, Georgia for more opportunities. Both pursuers of their entrepreneurial dreams, they wanted to invest in importing and exporting to take advantage of the riches Augusta had to offer by virtue of being located near the Savannah River ports and the Atlantic Ocean. Lexius Sr. had two boys by the names of Lexius Jr. and Harper. It is unknown if Charles had any children.

Harper married and had twelve children, which is vital in the union of my newly discovered family and this story. One of his grandchildren, Gertrude, married a man with the last name King. From this union, Krystal was born five generations later. I am Krystal's cousin. We met online, both seeking information about Lexius Henson. Lexius was where both of our trees had missing limbs. I could not replace meeting my cousin with a ton of gold.

Krystal's side of the family had migrated to the West Coast and parts of the Midwest. I was raised in Cleveland, Ohio. Both families lived comfortable lives, with strong beliefs in higher education and much success achieving their personal dreams.

Krystal and I are both nomads, always seeking new experiences and life's lessons. Her demeanor is very similar to that of my mother's, very compassionate, but with a no-nonsense personality, believing in expressing herself without apprehension. When she is displeased with a situation, you will know it. Like my mother, she will put the situation in order, not wasting words while making you understand her thoughts on the matter. I am told by my children that I spare no feelings as well; however, I don't believe this to be true, though I am to the point. Ironically, Krystal favors my mother's sister, Michelle. I look forward to meeting my cousin, Krystal, in person. I love saying "my cousin." Before, I was limited to using that term for my father's side. Krystal is now working on a PhD in, what else, genealogy research.

My mother did not know of any family from her Augusta past other than the Pryor side. Krystal only knew of the King family tree, with its missing lineage. Krystal knew Harper Henson was the grandfather of Gertrude and brother to Lexius Jr. Mom only knew Constance, Uncle P.R., my uncle Raleigh Borum, and a cousin named Willy. Raleigh, too, would try to help Mom piece together as much history as the two could muster together.

If Constance and Uncle Raleigh were not in my mother's life, the state of her mind would be unknown. They fill such voids in her existence. Thanks to Krystal, my mother was able to talk to her first cousin, David King, one of the oldest family members, before he passed. My mother is now one of the oldest living on her side of the family at the tender age of ninety-two.

The offspring of Gertrude King birthed a family of more than one hundred people. Thank God for Gertrude, who kept the family going. I am also thankful for Harper, my great-uncle, the brother of my great-grandfather, Lexius Jr. Lexius Jr. only bore Mattie and Hugh. Uncle Son did not have any children and his sister, Mattie, only had two, my aunt Michelle and my mom. Michelle did not have any children as well. My mother had eight. I was her fifth born, the middle child, the one the family always says is crazy.

My mother always thought she was the last of her family. I feel that is why she had so many children. At present, our side is just reaching the fourth generation because of my siblings. I don't believe we have yet reached one hundred family members to continue my mother's legacy. My father's side is another story. There are too many relatives to count, and I thank God for them. Krystal has shown me there are many, many limbs on the King family tree and the limbs are still sprouting.

Krystal and I will persevere on this journey that I believe was placed upon us by Lexius Henson Sr.'s restless soul. I feel him inside of me and I have visited him many times while writing this book. His spirit has overtaken my pen. It is as if I go back in time and sit at his knee as a learned child, seeking our lineage, our family knowledge, and the reasons why we yearn for the things we do.

Krystal has the same fervor that I possess and a burning desire to unite this clan, with no other motivation than unification of a family. Her research and dedication to this plight has been incredible. We've both always had the feeling that we came from higher breeding, with much richness in our family tree. Unbeknownst to us, the value was monetary as well. We do not seek endowments. What we seek cannot have a price tagged to it. When Krystal and I meet, I want to give her the gift of this book.

I go back and read my writings, sometimes days or weeks later, and I realize that I was only a vessel in the telling of this story. At one point, it seemed as if I had physically manifested into my great-great-grandfather's realm. Lexius dictated his journal to me and I didn't miss a word. His knowledge was vast, and he didn't spare many words when making a point, yet there was so much compassion in his heart.

As you read this story, it may touch home in a lot of your lives and families. If you are one of those who has made a similar choice to deprive someone of their natural life, whether by divorce, bad blood, or just a simple disagreement that seemed huge at the time, I beg of you to reconsider, forgive, don't deprive a legacy to someone that was never given a choice in the matter. It is a radiating hate, festering inside, which becomes a full-blown cancer, and the result is an early, miserable demise.

The Assyrians and many other cultures believe that you are a direct product of genes and not just your environment. Life, as trying as it is, should not be affected by lack of family lineage. As an American culture, we put no real value on the cause and effect of this real thing called heritage, failing to honor it as most other cultures do. Almost every nation in the world puts this life determining factor in front of all things.

The time has come for us to unite our souls for the betterment of self, which will perpetuate and transcend to all mankind. It is time for the unification of family and values. It is time for the unification of a race—the human race. This is just one story of family deprivation, heritage, and lineage. This was part of my living experience. Now, I will go back as far as I can to the root of the Henson family saga.

CHAPTER 2
Liz

My mother, Mary Elizabeth Pryor Rush, known as Elizabeth or Liz, was a beautiful child, with flawless features and hair with a reddish hue that reached down to the bend of her back. She had long, agile legs and a glowing personality. As she sat on the lap of her uncle, P.R. Pryor, a distinguished man of strong stature, who was black as coal, she sang a tune that her uncle often sang to tease her, "Redhead, gingerbread, five cents a cabbage head ..."

Uncle P.R. was the brother of Hattie, Liz's grandmother, and wife of Lexius Henson, Jr. P.R. was a tall, well-dressed man who noticeably ate well. He was an important man in the community as the superintendent of Pilgrim Insurance and Securities Company as well as an underwriter. He also served as committee chair for the Augusta, Georgia Committee for the Advancement of Negroes. He was heavily involved in the Reconstruction Era and he was known for carrying a pistol, and he was not afraid to use it.

Liz changed clothes three times a day and even though she was living during the Great Depression, she never had to experience it. Liz was quite cultured for a child of those times, having been exposed to dance, theater, sports, and the best education at Lucy Laney Institute, as well as private teachings.

"Who is my daddy, Uncle P.R.? Aren't you my daddy? Why do I call you Uncle?" asked the inquisitive and rambunctious child.

P.R. told Liz, "Slow down. Hold onto your horses on the interrogation. I will start by telling you that your great-grandfather was a very rich and powerful man of his time."

Liz, now on the edge of her chair, eagerly waited to hear more.

P.R found himself having to often change the subject due to the sensitive nature of Liz's heritage. Unbeknownst to her, Liz was mulatto. P.R. and his wife were responsible for her primary care. Liz's mother, Mattie Lee, had been having problems and was unable to fulfill the capacities of motherhood.

P.R. was given a temporary reprieve as the neighbor, Mr. Johnson, approached the yard. Liz jumped off her uncle's lap and stood behind her fortress, stating, "Here comes the neighbor, and he looks mad!"

As he approached, Mr. Johnson asked, "Mr. Pryor, do you know anything about my turtle disappearing?"

"Would you like a glass of tea?" asked P.R.

Mr. Johnson, ignoring the offer, continued to inquire about the whereabouts of his prized sixty-pound turtle.

P.R. reached into his pocket and kept his hand there.

Liz knew what was in the pocket, and it wasn't candy or tobacco. Liz ran into the house on her long legs in what seemed like one stride.

"Now, Mr. Johnson, back to the turtle," stated P.R. "You mean the one without a nametag on it? The one that wandered into my yard? The big one that would bring me good money on the market? It will be on the Pryor's menu tonight, and you are more than welcome to enjoy it with us for supper."

Mr. Johnson, outraged by P.R.'s boldness, lunged toward him, forgetting about P.R.'s hand in his pocket. Before he realized it, Mr. Johnson was about to eat the military pistol that P.R. had almost put into his mouth.

Liz ran out the door to stop her uncle, knowing she had a calming effect on him. Before she could reach him, all she could see was the back of Mr. Johnson's head and his elbows slicing the wind as he cussed with precision, kicking red dirt all the way home.

P.R., realizing Liz had possibly witnessed the exchange, changed his demeanor immediately and called out to Mr. Johnson with a smirk. "See you at supper. The soup will be divine."

Liz knew not to ask about the turtle. P.R. had educated Liz on the ways of the world in many incidents. She immediately shrugged off what had just transpired and went back to the interrogation concerning her ancestry. "Uncle, you were getting ready to tell me about my great-granddaddy."

P.R. thought the episode with Mr. Johnson had thwarted another inquisition, but not with Liz, and he had taught her to be that way so he could not get angry with her.

CHAPTER 3
UNCLE P.R.

Liz maneuvered her way back to P.R.'s lap.

"Liz, I just want you to know your great-grandfather was a very wealthy man. Lexius Henson, Sr. was one of the richest men in the South. He came from South Carolina with his brother, Charles. Lexius was a tall, handsome man of olive complexion, except when someone upset him; then he stayed as red as a ripe tomato until his problem was solved, kinda like you, Liz." Uncle chuckled as Liz pinched him gently. He continued. "I used to say he was a white man by day and a black man by night because of the many hats he had to wear. Lexius was mulatto. Lexius was a very educated man, book wise and worldly. He was always reading and his thirst for knowledge never ceased. When he spoke, people wanted to listen and he had quite a sense of humor with close friends as well as his patrons. It is not known what he did before his exodus to Augusta. It was known, though, that he took interest in his father's medical practice. On occasion, he had to show his knowledge on the matters

29

of medicine. He came from a very comfortable living. Lexius had a strong presence and voice, but he usually spoke in a melodious tone. He was always dressed to a T. He did not believe in acquiring a vast wardrobe, but what he had was of the finest quality. He owned monogrammed shirts and underwear and always a pair of cufflinks to match. He had tie clips made of the finest gold that glittered like stars in the night under the ambiance of his restaurant setting. His buttons were made of pearls and he wore pure silk shirts.

His speech was so eloquent and meticulous, it sounded like he spoke in a rhythmic beat. If you were fortunate to share an entire conversation, it was an enlightenment. He was a man that only spoke facts, even though he had great wit. He stirred your mind like one of the fine items on his delectable menu. People loved his company and his vast knowledge of the law and many other subjects. He was a hard worker and a visionary. He came up with ways to make everything he encountered better and more profitable. It's uncertain if his culinary skills came from formal training or were self-taught, but his restaurant was considered one of the best in the country and was compared to the finest restaurants abroad.

He started the restaurant saloon with his brother Charles in a building shared by Smythe & Blythe Brokerage Firm at 405 Broad Street in Augusta. The first day he moved in, he was already thinking of expansion. Lexius Sr. had his irons in a lot of fires, but his true strength was catering to others. He made it a point to ensure that every morsel of food eaten at his place would not be forgotten and was a savory experience that diners would anticipate during their next visit. Patrons tended to stick with the first dish they'd tried, thinking nothing else on the menu could be as delectable or insatiably mouthwatering; so Lexius, being the businessman he was, would bring out samples of other specialties. He knew that teasing patrons with samples of his vast selections would bring them back again and again, and just when they thought they'd had all Lexius had to offer, he would come up with a new dish or recipe. One time, he created a dish with escargot, mussels, and four different cheeses and coined it 'muscargot.' Patrons lost their minds over this exotic mixture. Lexius couldn't keep enough mussels and snails on hand.

He had the freshest produce, meat, fish, and wild game birds, as well as imported fruits. The only old items on the menu at Lexius's restaurant were the cognacs and other fine liquors he readily stocked. Even his ales were aged."

P.R. was the brother-in-law of Lexius's son, Lexius Jr. His sister, Hattie Pryor, married Lexius Jr. He had very strong ties to Lexius Sr. and he was as wise a businessman as Lexius Sr. He'd been entrusted to many financial dealings. He also served as a keeper of secrets.

P.R. would've loved to tell Liz of all the stories in his head, but she was too young for the truths he would never reveal. Gentlemen of the South bore a lot of secrets. P.R. always came up with some excuse when interrogated by Liz about her true history. He kept her mind and body preoccupied with social activities. She was highly intelligent; her thought process reminded P.R. of that of Lexius Sr. He believed Lexius Sr. to be reincarnated into her soul.

It was as if Liz already knew the answers to her questions but wanted validation. Liz had seen how other children lived at a lower standard than she was accustomed to. The cultural foundation of coming from money had been defined in Liz, so even if she didn't have a dime in her purse, no one would detect it. She once commented that she'd heard a group of kids talking about the last time they'd had meat on their plates. They were standing in front of the butcher's place, salivating. He would sometimes give them scraps to take home. Liz had said to P.R., "We have meat at every meal served, starting with breakfast."

Liz had a very kind heart.

P.R. had caught her a few times placing meat and other morsels into her linen napkin. She literally wept as she explained that it bothered her at night when she went to bed with a full stomach, complete with dessert and a bedtime snack of milk and cookies or pie, and some children didn't have meals, let alone meat and dessert in a month of Sundays. Lexius Sr. was the same, although he would never let anyone see him weep. That is why every Thanksgiving and Christmas, Lexius made sure there was a turkey on the peoples' tables, finding the biggest ones imaginable, which meant they would have meat on their plates for many meals after the holiday.

P.R. explained to Liz that the world was made of have and have nots and they could not save the whole world, but it was okay to do their part. They'd do what they could to help the unfortunate. Liz's heart of gold struggled to understand that, just like Lexius Sr. Many people never knew that charitable side of Lexius. He purposely kept it that way.

Lexius Sr. once explained to P.R. that the dynamic of the haves and have nots was just the order of the world; the imbalance was necessary to keep order, though he never fully agreed with that way of thinking. Lexius had stated, "It has been this way for a very long time in all cultures, since the beginning of mankind."

P.R. had made provisions for Liz to be comfortable, at least until the days of her adulthood. He couldn't promise what happened to his estate after his death. Lexius Sr. provided means to have meat on the table and keep his dowry intact, but things changed, people changed. Money had that effect. He could not guarantee anything but the end, as they say.

As Liz's mind soaked up all that P.R. was telling her, suddenly she switched the conversation, as she often did. "Uncle P.R., the girls at school said I was white. I told them I can't be white because you're black as coal," she stated.

P.R. immediately said, "Hold on, Liz," with a face full of embarrassment.

But Liz interjected by saying, "You are the most handsome man I've seen. Let's finish talking about Lexius." Liz always planted seeds of thought at the weirdest times.

She was a very talkative girl, and P.R. could see a lot of Lexius in her. His conversations would change as quickly as the last one came. Her mind never rested. Liz did not understand the words "no" or "can't"; that was Lexius!

P.R. continued. "Lexius Sr. was very good with his money. That's why he lived upstairs from his establishment. His living conditions were quite impressive. He was a very private person. He had the taste of royalty and was a very regal man, yet he could and would pull up his sleeves and get down and dirty if need be. Lexius parted seas as he walked. The women swooned over him, with his thick, bushy mustache, curly hair, and lean, slender build. Lexius never showed fear; he couldn't afford to.

Lexius was not well liked amongst his own people because

he did not serve Negros. It was amazing to see all the rich and famous people give him their respect. He transcended all color lines because of his character and the services he rendered. He hosted royalty, presidents, generals, and some of the richest people in the world. They respected him for his talents as well as his knowledge, business savvy, and wisdom. He was very smart in conversation, business, and he was a smooth talker."

Liz interjected laughingly, "Oh, like you, Uncle."

P.R. responded, "Liz, go on in there and get some peach cobbler."

As Liz skipped away, singing, "Redhead, ginger bread, five cents a cabbage head," P.R. chuckled to himself. "That girl got the savvy of her great-grandfather and don't know it. Lord … Lord … Help me."

P.R. thought he may have thrown Liz off track with the cobbler; however, when Liz returned, she was full of questions. She asked, "Why didn't I get to meet Lexius Sr., or Jr., or did I? Did they love me like you do, Uncle P.R.?"

The questions Liz asked were of a sensitive nature. P.R. really had no answers for those two questions that Liz would understand at her age. Liz's mother, Mattie Lee, had her out of wedlock, but Liz was never without a father—P.R. They made sure that Liz never went without.

P.R. told her, "Liz, go up and change for supper."

She was such a loving child but so much like Lexius Sr.; she wouldn't stop until she understood.

P.R. kept Liz's mind off those questions by keeping her busy. Liz's belly was always full and she got plenty of sweets, too many. P.R. spoiled that child. She was his pride and joy, and he knew she thought the world of him. She motivated him to do things for their race, for their world, to bring equality, heritage, and love to all people so P.R. would no longer have to sidestep her questions about her background. She made him work hard for all mankind. There were too many secrets robbing their race, not just their race, but the human race. Lexius's dream, as well as the secrets of their ancestors, were being denied, swept under the rug, never to be revealed. Their ancestral rights, the love of a relative of a different color or ethnic background, were unable to be revealed.

P.R. was a chairman for civil rights so we wouldn't have to keep secrets, so we could be proud, with no division. He was not taught to hate the white man, but to fear him. The white man was taught to hate *and* fear him. They all went to church and prayed to the same God, but they couldn't go to the same church. Even within the Negro race, there were light-skinned churches and dark-skinned churches. Negroes were divided and P.R. had to do what he could to unite us under God and the belief that we are all God's children.

He wanted to shield Liz from prejudice so she would not be inhibited by color barriers or believe she was of an inferior race. Liz was being raised as a Negro but she was actually of mulatto descent. She was neither white nor black; she was both. She was at that age where she asked a lot of questions. P.R. had his work cut out for him. He hoped to live long enough to see some of his seeds blossom and bear fruit. He could see that it was going to be a long journey, though. Hopefully, the northerners could help expedite these matters, preventing the seeds of hate from being too deeply planted. They had the backing of a couple of wealthy Europeans, Rockefeller, and Carnegie, two of the wealthiest men in the world.

There seemed to be groups that were honest and true to the Negro plight, without hidden agendas: the NAACP, the Urban League, and the YMCA. They had a group of very proud black people there in the area. Georgia, for the most part, used to be free until the king had sent the bottom of the barrel to the state when they saw the opportunity to capitalize on slavery. Everyone seemed to coexist in Augusta. Lynching still occurred, but the Negroes fought back.

Liz had told P.R. she wished she had his beautiful black skin (Liz could pass for European). She'd caught P.R. off guard. He told her that her color was as beautiful as his and that all God's colors were beautiful like His rainbow. She asked her uncle why black wasn't in the colors of the rainbow. She'd gotten him again, but he told her if she looked hard, she could see it at the top or the bottom.

P.R. wanted Liz to know all the answers to her questions because one day she was going to find out about the prejudices of the world. She was so beautiful and she was treated like a princess by all, not a black princess or a European princess, just a princess. They all should've been able to experience the same royal treatment, all being the children of a king.

CHAPTER 4
LIZ AND CONNIE

"Elizabeth, what is that you are hiding behind your back?"
"Nothing, Uncle P.R.," replied Liz.

She was called Elizabeth only when she was committing mischievous actions. Behind Liz's back was a photo of a woman and a man who appeared to be of regal heritage. It was a photograph she had been told not to disturb, kept in her uncle's room. That made the mystery of the picture even more intriguing to this rambunctious red-headed child of nine. Liz was raised as an only child, with the imagination of a little girl seeking companionship and amusement. She was not allowed in the room where the portrait seemed to call her name every time she passed it, the room that was as grand as the photograph. She often played in the forbidden room when Uncle P.R. was away. Many times, she had come close to being discovered in this room. Liz had yet to take the time to muse at the photograph before she was caught by Uncle P.R. She bolted like a rabbit being chased by a dog back into the forbidden part of the house to replace the mystical picture in the room. Uncle P.R. was not agile enough to chase her.

Liz darted past Auntie as she was preparing supper. It was getting late into the evening, when the beautiful Augusta sun was about to settle into the background of a scenic summer day.

Constance, nicknamed Connie, was one of her best friends. Liz spent much time in Connie's home and Connie considered her a sibling, as most families did in that era with each other's children and extended family. They believed in the old saying "It takes a village to raise a child." That was a good thing, except when Liz or Connie got into trouble. They were the recipients of the switch on several occasions, even before they'd made it home. In those days, the neighbor that caught you was allowed to use the switch as they walked you home to receive another lashing. They were inseparable and of good breeding. They had a wondrous imagination between the two of them. Connie's mother and father were present in her household. Uncle P.R. and Auntie were the only parents Liz knew. Because she was raised by secondary parents, Liz was quicker to get the switch at Connie's house than at home.

There were a lot of questions in Liz's mind as to the whereabouts of her real father and why her mother wasn't present, but it was a topic not spoken about or questioned. In those days, many were raised by other family members, neighbors, or those with the means to do so. Family, in those days, was not determined by the bloodline.

Liz didn't know how close she was to the reality that she was royalty, the great-granddaughter to one of the most unknown, but known, famous people of Georgia, the South, and the world.

CHAPTER 5
BACK TO LIZ

"That certainly was an excellent meal, Auntie and Uncle P.R. Did you make a pecan pie too, Auntie? That peach cobbler was so, so good! I picked a lot of pecans for you today. Did you want me to take some to the neighbors?" Liz rattled off. There were about five or six pecan trees on the property. "Uncle P.R., are you going to finish that story?" Liz asked.

Uncle P.R. pinched Liz under the table.

Auntie was putting away food when she heard Liz scream, "Ouch!" She asked, "What is wrong, Elizabeth?"

Uncle P.R. pinched her again and promised her a big slice of pecan pie.

"Nothing, Auntie," said Liz. "Uncle stepped on my toe."

Liz got the message and whispered to P.R., "Well, are you going to tell me the rest of the story about my grandfather? Please, please, Uncle!"

P.R. replied, "After you help clear the table and all of your business is taken care of. Child, I taught you to never beg for anything. Go get me the *Chronicle.*"

Uncle was accustomed to sitting on the beautiful, spacious sun porch after supper in his favorite wicker rocking chair as he watched the evening settle. Liz imagined he was sitting on a mighty throne. Someone was always speaking to P.R. or stopping by to say good evening as they took their evening constitution, that is if Uncle gave a favorable nod of the head, indicating it was okay to approach and enter the gate. It all depended on what type of day P.R. had. P.R. was a very strong man of stature. He did not tolerate munch nonsense and the community knew it.

P.R. was like putty in Liz's hand. Liz knew that she got away with a lot of things. She thought she was pulling the wool over P.R.'s eyes, but he knew all that she did. She was no stranger to the strap. They usually saw Mr. Johnson, the turtle owner, strolling when the sun was falling. But for the past few days, he had not appeared. She didn't know if that was because of personal fear because of the turtle incident or if it was a direct command by P.R. not to come into proximity of the house. This would not be the first time this edict would've been placed upon a neighbor.

They sometimes had boarders, so peddlers would sometimes come by to sell their wares. P.R. didn't tolerate this most of the time. He did not allow his boarders to be harassed unless their presence was requested by the tenant, with P.R.'s permission.

It was as if P.R. could smell the different passersby. He would appear to be totally engrossed in the *Chronicle* or whatever he was reading, with his face shielded. So and so would pass by and he would call them by name without lowering the paper. Liz would just sit and watch to see if he'd peeked around the paper or if it had a hole in it, or something. She never unmasked his seemingly magic powers.

It was truly a treat to be in his presence. He was a very educated man, from lessons taught and books he'd read. He was quite an authority on most subjects and made sure that one day Liz's knowledge would be even greater than his. P.R. made sure that Liz was well read and cultured in the ways of the world. He kept her involved in all of the events that were proper for a child of her social stature.

P.R. kept Liz under close watch. She sometimes had to sneak away to play and get into mischief like other kids in the community. On occasion, she played with her imaginary friend. Auntie was as dear to Liz as her uncle. It was pretty much her job to take care of Liz.

She used to reap many benefits from being P.R.'s child whenever she was in town. Other adults would give her free candy, fruits, and other things and tell her to make sure she said hello to P.R. on their behalf. She was not allowed to take anything unless Auntie gave a nod of her head.

She felt quite special being his child. For many years, P.R. ran boys away from courting her. Even though she was taught to be of social awareness, to be a little lady at all times, she had a little tomboy in her that P.R. did not celebrate. At the same time, she saw a little gleam in his eyes because she was able to take care of herself with boys and girls. After all, he'd taught her those lessons as well. It was not just a rumor that Uncle P.R. kept his pistol close by. When it was not by him, Liz knew it was in the china cabinet and she also knew how to fire it.

P.R. was known to keep a lot of cash on him, for he was a policy collector at one point and a superintendent for the Plymouth Insurance Company. Liz later found out that he was the trustee for many people's estates and executor to some well-to-do people. Money, clothing, food, and the finer things in life were never an issue, even though Liz saw many others who were less fortunate. P.R. was shrewd with money and investments, but he also had a very compassionate side for the rights of others. He believed in giving respect and receiving it in return. P.R. taught Liz to be expressive but always respectable.

P.R. taught her the value of honesty and being of good character, to be a careful listener as well as a speaker. One of his favorite quotes was from Abe Lincoln: "It's better to remain silent and be thought a fool than to open up your month and remove all doubt." He taught Liz not to be a borrower or lender, which was in the Good Book. Church was a must for maintaining the opposition of temptation.

THE JOURNAL
OF
LEXIUS HENSON, SR.

CHAPTER 6
SHIP OF DESPAIR

Dear Journal,

Today the "Ship of Despair," as I have named it, has arrived, and more souls, lineage, and heritage will be separated. People in my community do not believe this event severely affects me. The slaves are hoarded to a holding area like common stock. The only highlight of this event for the slaves is that they are finally fed properly and somewhat clothed and bathed. The slave traders would feed them well for fear they'd pass out like sickened calves or steer. The auctioneers group them by gender, age, and stamina. The women are sold as good potential breeders, cooks, and farm help. One's child can be an asset or hindrance, depending upon the needs of the buyer. The strong male bucks are the best sell. They pry open the mouths of the stock like horses or cattle. The auctioneers approximate the slaves' ages and working capabilities.

The women's breasts are usually exposed to entice the master or the agent representing the master to pay a higher price. They believe a big, healthy one can breastfeed two at the same time, while tending the field. They could also fulfill the master's midnight requests for the Nubian slave to enter his stable of lust and infidelity. The plantation owners like them young, budding their flowers of womanhood. They love the big hips of the African women, yet they make their wives who may have large posteriors hide their backsides because it is an embarrassment to the Europeans, as it may reflect some type of relationship to the Negro.

Now, a child born from this union of master and slave may vary in physical structure. Some of the women born of this interracial union maintain posteriors of definition while others are somewhat flattened. The union of both races, though, usually creates a beautiful child, a mulatto. These mulattoes are normally given favor by the masters and abhorred by their own darker relatives. The master, I have observed, loves the dissention this causes amongst the Negroes. It keeps them at odds within their community. It keeps them fighting, or, should I say, divided, which keeps their minds off of revolt. What really perplexes me is that the hate of the Africans toward their oppressors is different from the hate some Europeans have for the Negro. The Negro's hate is not malicious. The Negro really doesn't have the time or luxury for that emotion. Their thoughts are too consumed by survival. I cannot even imagine being separated from my family.

There are, what you may call, experts on maintenance and raising slaves, who counsel plantation owners. The West Indies has been a leading example. I have overheard their strategies on many occasions in my establishment. Separate the old from the young, strong from the weak, lighter from darker. Very few families are kept together after the sale, the exception being when a female slave is with child or has an infant child. The larger males are used as bucks to repopulate with stronger offspring.

I have been told that African tribes sell other tribes that they have conquered, and this is not hard to believe. In the Bible, this practice occurred as a norm. Slavery has been around since forever, but that does not make it justifiable. This practice is deeply rooted in the world. There are divisions of race and beliefs, yet we are all of the human race. There was Adam and Eve, so if you believe in the Bible, how could you not believe that we are all of the human race? I understand that not all cultures believe in the Bible or practice the teachings of the Bible, but almost all religions that I have studied believe in God, creator of heaven and earth, and that at first there was man and there was woman, starting our lineage. Even if you believe that we evolved from apes, it would still mean that we were all derived from the same species, the same tree.

We have a devout following of Christians here in the South on Sunday, but on Sunday night, the blessed Sabbath day, white men are lynching or tarring and feathering Negroes or Negro lovers. I cannot begin to share all of the atrocities I have witnessed and overheard and know to be factual. In the event this journal is ever discovered, its intent is not to cause malice or incite hate, but to bring our human race to enlightenment. Live and let live in harmony. Love one another.

It saddens me to be unable to do anything about slavery. The ones who are purchased by the local plantation owners are more apt to live a better existence. There had been a more cohesive relationship here in Augusta between the Negro and the European before slavery. Augusta and South Carolina were heavily populated by mulattoes. It was legal in South Carolina to marry outside of your race. Negroes were free in this state until the king sent his derelict rejects to this region and they saw an opportunity to capitalize. They were thieves, murderers, bottom-of-the-barrel citizens in their own country, yet still superior to the Negro in this new country.

My visiting patrons brag and compare their different methods of controlling their slaves. On auction weeks, my business is overwhelmed by these traders of souls. I do not favor my clientele during that period. My patrons are normally people of culture and long heritage, and possess some sort of humanism. The people I receive when the ships come in are of very questionable backgrounds. They are hired by the plantation owners to be buyers or agents, as they are called. They are of temporary financial means. They usually leave my place broke and with heavy heads.

These agents are so crass and obnoxious that my usual clientele is embarrassed by their presence. Many times, I've had to endure their ignorance. I had to send for the sheriff on many occasions during the week of "Separation of Souls." It is somewhat reassuring, and I loosely use that term, when my patrons of character do not try and co-exist with these sorts. It tells me that one day there may be parity amongst races; at least this is a dream of mine. Believe it or not, I have heard these same sentiments between the Europeans while under the influence of whiskey and cognac. What we have here in Augusta is quite a unique situation regarding different races.

I overheard one of the slave agents referring to his plans to partake in the pleasures of the female slaves he had just purchased. He was bragging as if he had just returned from a safari in Africa and was literally about to mount his trophies. It made me sick to my stomach, along with some of my normal patrons, who cordially exited my establishment. My patrons have apologized for the crassness of these agents. Some have even offered to have these men dealt with. In the South, there are many men of honor; they are sympathetic to the Negro. They are businessmen, who are pressured by other counties and states to agree with the inhumane treatment and use of the Negro and not just the Negro, but also the less fortunate people of European descent who are treated, at times, worse than the Negro. They, too, experience separation of souls and are ripped from their families to share in the black hole of lineage. This group of people are sympathetic to the Negro but you have those who are worse off than the Negro but still feel superior; they are called "poor white trash," or as I say it, "lighter economical equals."

As far as I can tell, these sorts who carry out these heinous crimes sleep well at night, if not better, after a lynching. How can that be? A person who cannot stand another race will let their children be breastfed by the same one that they abhor. They eat their cooking and have relations … It is just mind boggling. This is total irrational thought and behavior, yet the slave is considered to be the one incapable of logical thought and humanism. This separation of souls has been the product of just a few ill-guided philosophies that are not even of this country. Polygenism is the term coined for the justification of conquering and enslaving what is perceived to be a lesser race. This way of thinking has been beneficial for the few who truly profit from this sick way of existence. Those of the same race who perpetuate these ungodly acts are not as well off as the Negroes, Indians, or Asians, but they will not acknowledge that fact. They are being used as tools as well, even more so than the slave. They are as expendable as the minority who are being manipulated. They, too, are being used in a game, like pawns in a game of Chess, a game which I have mastered—the game of life. I will vent further on this matter later on.

I, at no time, think that I am in a position of hierarchy because of my financial means and status in this region. I know that I am as vulnerable as the next. My awareness has taught me to play the same game of Chess that they play, but better. Always staying moves ahead is the key to victory in this game as well as anticipation and observing strategies. I probably would be considered the bishop piece on the board. Trusted with knowledge, allowed to make observations, but still limited to the diagonal direction I am allowed to move. Only the king and queen can move in any direction, and I am far from being honored with that title. Only a select few are, and a lot of them have frequented or graced my establishment with their presence (I use grace facetiously).

The king and queen have to build a castle, a moat, an army, a defense against treachery, deceit, and defeat. Until we all realize that we will be manipulated as merely pieces on a board, we will be defeated. Yes, life does require a king and a queen, but there can also exist a fairness. Everyone, by God's creation, is not designed to rule. In God's divine order is love, equality, and freedom. The divine order was not designed to have an imbalance of rights, the right to treat people as if they were a lesser part of God's creation. God even takes care of the sparrow. Yes, everyone has a different purpose for their existence, a different hierarchy on the tree of life, but all are essential in the growth of the tree. If one exists without the other, there is no tree, no roots, trunk, leaves, seedlings, fruit, etc. We must all come together and accept our existence. A tree is nothing without the aforementioned attributes in addition to the sun, the soil, and water. This is the culmination of life; the human race is the ultimate example.

My concern is how many generations will not know their meaning in life, their reason for existence, because their heritage has been stripped away from them. I truly believe that which is inherited in your bloodline is a major determining factor in your future and destiny. As a result, we will wander without direction, with no foundation of character. From what I have heard, this is the goal of those who are in control. I have tried to alert those in the realm of my circle, but I am very limited because I, myself, ride the fence of righteousness, not for ill-gotten gains, but for my heritage and position in the community

The depth of my thoughts will probably never be purveyed, only to you, Journal, and my kin from another age, whom I feel is present. I hope this knowledge will be entrusted unto you.

———————

It is a rainy night
My thoughts are in flight
They hum like a bird
 But I wonder if my words will ever be heard
So much to say
So much going on in my day
I try to harness my thoughts
But will it all be for naught?
If my journal is ever revealed
I wonder if those with another plan lay in wait, only
to steal
My mission is not that of the commission
Those that rule, they are complacent when I wear
the harness of a mule
I am of both worlds
My race was not created by my choice
I am a silent voice
I am of another dominion
With a total different outlook and opinion
I see both sides
My feelings I am forced to hide
Will we ever unite?
My character is different by night
What is going on in this world seems to be a

senseless plight

We continue to fight, fight, fight

Will there be light at the end of the tunnel

Or are we just a liquid in a funnel

My soul has such a void because of all the stories
that will not be told

Oh, my God, how many souls were sold?

Nobody knows my origin

They always ask about my religion

With this information, they feel they can place my race

They have such a puzzled look on their face

My color is not black

It is not brown; it is not white, nor is it yellow

They wonder, "Who is this fellow?"

I become a threat

Because to their friends who have inquired

They have just lost the bet

I am of the human race

Take a moment and look at my face

My body as well

I have two eyes, two ears, two lips, two hips

Two arms, two legs, two feet, ten toes

And the same nose

Only different in shape

Why now is your mouth agape?

The only difference is in thought

Because you have allowed it to be bought

I am you

You are me

All originated from the same tree ...

Let us all be free

CHAPTER 7
MY FORTRESS

Dear Journal,
   My investments in tobacco and rice are beginning to pay off. I have put monies into tobacco export as well. They now have machines that roll cigarettes and can mass produce at a quicker rate and with less labor costs. More people are smoking now. It has become a fashionable thing. Smoking was limited to pipes and cigars prior to this invention. The female patrons in my establishment love to partake in a good cigar in their private parlors. It is entertaining to see them enjoying a good imported stogie as well as our comparable home-grown blends, especially when it is their first experience. Once they get past the first choke, they really seem to enjoy the clandestine ritual for women of elite stature. Some try to disguise the smell of the cigar with perfumes or they just blame it on the men. I burn exotic incense, mainly on the women's floor. I have some really intoxicating fragrances. Some are imported from as far as Egypt and Asia; the more favorable ones are from African regions, believe it or not. I sell the incense as well as fragrant candles

and different potpourris. Some of them, I have been told, have an aphrodisiac effect. Between the cigars, the fine cognacs and liquors, and cuisine, the ambiance seems to leave the female patrons with a euphoric, scintillating experience.

My protégé, John Hope, and my valets have been known to literally carry patrons to their carriages and doorsteps on occasion, after they've fallen victim to the royal riches I offer. I, at no time, encourage drunkenness or any form of lewdness, but the alcohol seems to have that effect on many. I don't ask John what occurs on these short trips to the patrons' abodes. I have always taught John the art of discretion. Even though the temptation is great and readily offered to my valets, I tell them not to jeopardize their livelihoods on a whim from a whisked woman. The husbands do not always leave the restaurant with their wives. What happens in my place stays in my place, and there have been some embarrassing and compromising situations here. It is a sight to see when the elite let their guard down. When the whiskey goes down, the stiff collars go up and the petticoats begin to ruffle. Once again, by no means do I endorse these goings on.

I am in no position, first of all, to question these aristocrats on their behavior, but we all share somewhat of a gentleman's agreement of no kissing and telling. My individual parlors are fit for kings or queens. The ambiance is incredible. One day, I would like for my wife and myself to be able to partake in the amenities that I offer.

Many of the wealthy choose to put on their gala events at my establishment instead of their portly estates. I make a very large profit when I cater these affairs. I have the finest linen, silverware, and crystal that money can purchase, along with a vast menu.

There are usually no special requests. My patrons rely solely on my taste and judgment. So many have to loosen not one, but two or more buttons after their dining experience.

I had been asked, initially, in my first restaurant endeavor, to have an establishment for men only and one where they could bring their wives or female friends. So I combined the thoughts and purchased the old *Augusta Chronicle Newspaper* building, a building large enough to accommodate these requests. I have an oyster bar, billiards room, and a bar on one floor for the men, a floor for the ladies, and a floor with parlors for both. It is all well furnished, fit for royalty. I have my own palatial palace on the top floor, which is my residence. Very few are allowed on this level. If people knew the riches of my palace, it would create a stir.

My abode is far greater than many of my wealthiest patrons. I keep up with all modern conveniences but maintain my establishment as well; it is really all I have to do with my money, Journal. I do not spend a lot of time in my palace though. My family does and they are quite comfortable. I have maids' quarters in the rear and they are very nice compared to today's standards. I also have nanny quarters. What I have, no one on the outside knows exists, except for the few who are entrusted to know. It can readily be turned into a fortress if necessary. As of yet, there has been no reason to fill the moat around my castle. I have quite a view of the neighborhood. I literally oversee my domain. At night's end (or for me, mornings), I go out on my roof veranda and stargaze. It is as if I could reach out and pluck the stars to give them as gifts or use as spices in my magical dishes. It is so serene up there. It is too incredibly magical and mystical to justifiably describe, but I will try.

———

The moon appears to be so close that I can have a conversation with its face and no one can hear us. He tells stories and I listen. As Mr. Moon rises, the sun sets off into the horizon, melting into the shape of the earth, replaced by the flickering lights that we call stars. The stars begin to light up individually, like soldiers at a roll call, each hollering out its existence. It is magical, the order, the discipline that the stars have. On occasion, which is very special to me, I see a star flying through the night like a slave fleeing from his imprisonment or someone's dream finally coming true, or a messenger warning troops. I know many star groups by their names. I call upon them as a sergeant would his troops. They always answer "Present," unless it's an unclear night. Then I imagine them out on a mission of a clandestine nature. I await the next night to see if they return unscathed. As the stars begin to dissipate, I see a glow. Could it be the ball of fire that melted the night before into the corners of the earth? As it rises, I feel the warmth in my soul, understanding that it is an existence that is far greater than me and any man. Many have not awakened to another exhibition of this incredible delight, but I am privileged, once again, to observe this miracle that is shared with me. I love the sunset as well as the sunrise. Both remind me that I am just little old me.

CHAPTER 8
THE EDGE OF FREEDOM

Dear Journal,

One of my entrees is crab. I purchase them by the barrel. I have blue belly and ocean crab. My ocean crab are so large that I had to make a special tub to steam them in. I spice them with paprika, a little garlic powder, lemon, butter, and some other secret ingredients. I melt some freshly churned butter with other ingredients for the patrons to dip the finished product in. I just sit back and listen to the moans of delight as they eat my crab by the barrel. I also sell them at the oyster bar and they sell well. On occasion, I have a contest to see who can eat the most. I learned quickly that this was an amusing but not a profitable event.

One day, as I worked my figures and prepared menus, I observed that the lid of the barrel was ajar. I saw a set of claws reaching out of the barrel. I thought the crab was about to escape but it fell back inside, even though it appeared to have had a fine grip on the rim of the barrel. I sat back and watched as another crab emerged on top of the one that had fallen back in. This cycle occurred repeatedly. I moved a little closer to make sure it wasn't the same crab reaching the top. To my amazement, it was a different crab each time. So I opened the lid all the way to see if the limited exiting space was the reason for the repetitive struggle to get out of the barrel at the expense of the other crab. I then observed that they did not try to escape at any other space on the rim. They took turns pulling each other down again and again.

At first glance, I was in awe that they worked together to use each other as a chain to reach the top. I found out, though, that this was not their ploy. There was no unity. They were preventing each other from escaping. They were on the edge of freedom. They were so close. I related this to the period in which I live (the Reconstruction Era). I relate this to both races as well. It reminds me of when a few Negroes came into my restaurant and challenged the new laws for serving Negroes. I am a Negro/mulatto, so why would they not go challenge a white person's place of business? I have constantly preached to my people that we must have unity in order to survive and flourish in this new world and times. I have expressed this cautiously to the whites as well when asked for my opinion on what is needed to make the South survive.

I have expressed my beliefs, not just for the South's survival, but for the world's survival. Man is his own worst enemy. I did not give up on the crabs in the barrel, for I knew there would be at least one strong enough to escape, and I promised myself that if one did escape, he would not be on the menu. I would set it free. I contemplated this theory about our race as well. It takes just one strong one to pave the way. It just takes one to say I am going to clear the path and build the road, but first and foremost, it requires vision.

I sat back for two hours in deep thought, literally coaxing on a winner. It never happened. I prayed that this was not a reflection of our lives in our world. This was an epiphany of my struggle. This became very perplexing to me. For now, I have to figure out how to get out of the barrel, as I thought I had already. In this moment of contemplation, I realized that I was the crab at the top of the barrel, about to be pulled back in if I did not figure out how to communicate to the others how we can all get out. This just added to more sleepless nights during my plight of the unification of the human race.

No one could possibly understand my strife, but maybe others lie awake at night with the same thoughts and dreams. At this point in time, there are only a few who stand out and share my quest. One lad shows much promise and that is John Hope. What a name to be given. They ask, "What's in a name," but I hope there will be a lot in reference to the name John Hope. He reminds me of myself. He's always asking questions, always wanting more. John can surely pass for one hundred percent European, but he chooses to own up to his mixed heritage. I am so proud of that.

I think I will drink some warm milk with a mild sedative and scrounge through the pantry. This usually relaxes me. Goodnight, my journal. Until we meet again … I bid you a good morning.

CHAPTER 9
IF MY SOUL COULD ONLY REST

Dear Journal,
I always have a watchman on duty so I am prepared. The newly formed Reconstruction Era group, primarily, was not a rowdy bunch. They did have a couple of ruffians and agitators amongst them. Once again, I am down for their cause, which is mine as well, believe it or not. I do not excuse myself from the fact that I, too, share their plight, but they do not believe I have the same interest in this civil movement as they do. I am not worried, but I take all threats seriously. I am certain they will try to rebel at my establishment again. Not to patronize or undermine them, I will offer them a drink, but not in my saloon. I would love to give them assistance for their strategies, but they will not take this aid from me. They just don't know how many of their lives I have already saved and bettered, and it saddens me, but I cannot reveal all to them.

They are like crabs in a barrel. We have enough Negro patrons to sustain a higher way of living in our community, with some of the finest commodities available. Some whites buy our wares. Negroes are allowed to shop in most of the white stores here in Augusta.

Many have told the small group of Negroes that they disagree with their choice to challenge the new law with me. Come Thanksgiving and Christmas, I will still be bringing their families turkeys, clothes, and gifts for the children and elderly. I try not to take this matter personally. I forgive, but I surely do not forget. My list of names has increased. I have to be concerned about the safety of my family and my staff. Some of my staff are related to those in that group. Kinship does not always relate to friendship.

I have learned to live with the label "white man by day, black man by night." I guess this title is self-explanatory, Journal, but the next time they need some liquor out the back door because the still blew up, they may be out of luck, or it may cost them double. The only things I turn down are my bed at night and my lamp. I am still a businessman. I am in the same boat with them. I, too, have a curfew at night. I, too, have had my papers in order when that day required it. I just happen to be very well known and I'm very rarely placed in such an awkward position to have to show my identity. I understand and have shared this experience as well. I have come within seconds of my life during travel to Savannah to do my catering. If it were not for a familiar face in the crowd, I might have succumbed to the end of the rope, a beating, or buckshot. I bleed the same as any other Negro man.

I am a Negro, too; I am of two colors, though. But in this land, one drop of African blood deems you Negro or white trash. The ones fathered by Europeans are named mulattos. We are sometimes looked upon as being worse than a Negro, like a mutt dog. It all depends on who is doing the judging. We are a race of our own at many times; nobody claims us. No one bothers to look at it from that perspective, so we have to be stronger than most could ever conceive. A Negro knows exactly where he stands in this land. We, however, have to stand by, wait, and listen for what may come out of someone's mouth to ascertain their belief or judgment of our skin.

That is why many mulattos have headed to California and the North to hide their identities. They start anew as Europeans and marry another European to strengthen their white genes, to eradicate the African blood inside of them. I wonder how many pasts are going to be erased as a result of hidden identities. So many family trees starting anew. So much history, so much lineage lost to racism within the same race, these different ways of thought. I do not encourage any of this in my tree, but I do not have control of this matter after I pass on. I will not discourage my children from marrying a darker person. This colorism is already taking place here in Augusta—mulattos only marrying mulattos. They even discriminate with their religious worship by only allowing mulattos into one church and Negroes in the others. It is sad that even religion harbors racism.

Where is the line drawn amongst Negroes and mulattos? I wonder many a night if I will have a legacy. There is someone who comes to me in my dreams, who I feel is of blood relation. We have earnest conversations about race and my lineage as if he, too, has a journal, but about my life. He, too, is so concerned about this racism thing. He has a very strange color; his hair is of my texture, with the same receding hairline, but his skin is of an orange or bronze hue. I don't know what color or race he is. Feet of bronze … Is it Jesus? Oh no, I'm not ready to go home yet. He is a much younger man than myself and he listens so intently to every syllable that I pronounce, like that of a child listening to stories while sitting on a grandparent's lap.

I hope his strange color represents the fact that my family did not try to hide their heritage and my future family is of all colors, the colors of the human race! His character has such a richness, like the character I have instructed my family to portray. I have taught them that even if they do not have a dime in their pocket to walk into a room as if they can buy it, but with humbleness. Education is the key to culture. Maybe I am a white man by day and a black man by night, but I could also be a black man by day and a white man by night. Journal, I must be tiring, but this weighs heavily on my heart, my soul, and my mind, and I must return to you at a later date on this subject matter. I hope my new friend returns as well. There is much more to be articulated on this matter. I have much deeper philosophies on this issue, which could be quite enlightening to the existence of the future in reference to race relations.

———————

Journal, I know it appears to you that I am always
in distress
But I have been placed here on this earth in a time
of duress.
If my soul could only rest.
Believe it or not, I always look for the silver lining
But others that are in control do the defining
And their rules are ever so binding.
If my soul could only rest.
I live in tumultuous times
And unity seems so far out of range
But we are the ones obligated to rearrange and
make this change.
If my soul could only rest.
I am only one being
And this era goes against all of the Almighty's seeing
We must all combine as one
Or this great world we live in will be done.
If my soul could only rest.
I am inspired by the divinity of God
     But they use human souls as a cattle prod.
I did my part, I guess this is a start
But I know it will not suffice, me being only one
device.
If my soul could only rest.
I am of a race that is undefined.
Will all of my efforts be undermined?
I come from good stock
But I only possess one key, when many, many doors
are locked
That could set us free.
If we could only unite against this plight.

Oh, what a struggle! What a fight!
If we could understand that there is only one plan
One race
The human race
One face
There is only one key to this kingdom.
And if we would follow only His plan and not let
our souls be so hollow in this land
The true Master has the only key to set us free.
If my soul could only rest.
If my soul could only rest.

———

Until we meet again, Journal. I bid you a good morning.

CHAPTER 10

BATTLEFIELD

Dear Journal,

It is a melancholy night. Spirits won't rest. All around me, destruction is going on, but at the same time, it is a reconstruction of the times. Will my family and I survive? Will this land survive? Destruction is so rampant, so prevalent. Will Augusta be annihilated like Atlanta? It is on Sherman's map of conquest, almost a straight arrow to the coast. I have seen the plans. I can hear the battles as clearly as I can hear my child. What a time to have brought a child into this world. What is in store for the future? I hear the plans of the future from great men that I encounter, but are they to be trusted or relied upon? I still truly believe that my God has the final say in this war.

There is no sound like that of a man screaming with his last breath. It touches your soul all the way to your bones. Your last breath … No chance to tell your loved ones that you love them or your last thoughts—a lonely demise. Your last breath, filled with pain and your whole life flashes in front of you. If you're lucky, you go in an instant, without the suffering, without seeing the bullet or the blade coming. What a restless afterlife that would be, but it is probably the way I would prefer to leave. What about the ones who had a painful death, suffering as their skin boiled, seared by iron pellets, radiating heat throughout their bodies, the heat of hell's brimstone within their veins? I am a strong man, but I cannot imagine this. So many widows, fatherless children, brothers, uncles, cousins, and best friends lost to a cause that may not even be justified.

But I once read in the Good Book that "there will be wars and rumors of wars until the end of time." Is this by man's design or the Higher Power? This war has been a scene of Armageddon. I pray that it is just a scene and not the whole play.

On occasion, we receive the wounded from both sides. So many are without limbs and eyes, but I will not go explicitly into the extent of the damage I have witnessed. We just try to make their last moments as painless as possible. We try to fulfill their last requests, usually just a letter they want to pass on to loved ones. The letters are more gut wrenching than witnessing their deaths. At times, you become a part of each letter and the family that is to receive this last will and testament. There are cousins killing cousins, uncles killing nephews, and brothers killing brothers. I've heard, in some instances, of fathers killing sons.

This is a war like no other I have read about in history. Will the future inhabitants of this land really understand the travesty of this war? I cannot judge whether this war is a necessary act. Will anyone be able to judge or justify this war as a necessary action? Rumor has it that the South has fallen and the Union will be triumphant.

You can smell the flesh all the way from Atlanta, the flesh of the land and that of man. Both sides have been very brutal in their methods of destruction. Women, children, and the elderly have been senselessly slaughtered and property has been destroyed and pilfered. A lot of the violence has been just an excuse, I believe, to vent ignorance and hatred. Many souls will go without rest. Many secrets of these atrocities will not be revealed. So much travesty, pain, fear, and torture. I am so blessed that Augusta has been passed over so far. My chest is full with anxiety and despair. I must maintain the appearance of courage and hope for those who look to me for guidance.

So many families have been divided. It is bad enough that many families were divided by slavery and illegitimacy. Now, we are divided by war, in most cases, for survival of a family name. Where does the division amongst the human race cease? It is ever so prevalent in this land. If we all knew of our common relation, war would be minimized. This, I see, is going to carry on well into the future, amongst the states that are yet to be united, if they ever will be.

My relative from another time tells me there will be a great number of states united in name only. The South will be the South and the North will be the North. United, but divided by individual beliefs. I guess that is why people came here, to be able to express their beliefs, even though freedom of thought depends on where you reside and being able to express your beliefs still exists in the future.

I have family that has already migrated west, as far west as you can go, to the coast of the Pacific Ocean. Some will pass for white and others are of a darker complexion. This, I believe, will inevitably cause the loss of family relations and heritage. I fear this greatly. Even though I have been accused of being a self-centered individual, this is far from the truth. I have always endorsed and emphasized family. Family is the only thing we have that is certain, or it should be. But in these days, that, too, has been compromised. Those who choose to leave the plantations for hope, for dreams of a more equal life, for freedom, flee to the North. Some families have encouraged the migration of the younger ones, while others have disowned family members for leaving their roots. Many are too old to make the journey to the North or out west, but they have given blessings to the change. You can't really blame those who don't flee. Fear is all they have known for their entire existence. All the young ones know are stories of freedom that are being rampantly spread, despite the myth that they will never be free.

The Negro is usually portrayed as shiftless and lazy. I beg to differ. If that were the case, there would not be so many wealthy white southerners. Some say this is only because the Negroes are watched over and constantly threatened to produce, but this is not so. They are a very proud race. They are a race that comes from a simple lifestyle, but a lifestyle that required everyone to be productive. Everyone in the African villages or tribes had to be able to contribute to the survival of their existence. They did it joyfully. They found and still find great rewards and pride in harvesting their skills. They are not filthy, unclean heathens by nature. Those who were unsavory were placed in unsavory conditions. They were called uncouth for things as simple as not combing their hair. Many European styles were thrust upon the African. The African believes highly in good hygiene. They know all the secrets of fragrances and incense and they relish in them. Many fragrances used at present come from the African tribes.

The Negro is very apt to learn, adapt, and improvise. The Negro has been forced to be innovative because of the limited resources that were allotted, but their innovation is a natural instinct as well. We have invented many things to better the ways of life. If the Negro didn't invent it, he improved upon it. Most of our inventions were stolen or purchased for the price of peanuts, but we are becoming more educated on these matters. The Negro is a very proud race. The Negro has won great battles for the Union.

I have drifted into other thoughts now, Journal, which is good. I had started out writing tonight in despair. Now, I have eased my thoughts somewhat. It is hard, though, when life around you is changing so rapidly, some of it for good and some of it for naught. I just try to make a difference with my existence on this planet. I am more spiritual than most know. The nature of my life does not allow me to reveal that side of myself, but it should show in my works. Until we meet again, Journal. I bid you good morning!

CHAPTER 11
CIVIL WAR

Dear Journal,
Death is all around Augusta. Sherman is still on his "March to the Sea." A lot of the Negros on paper are fleeing to Sherman's forces. They are taking every able-bodied male they can take on. They are using them for battle and menial tasks. They have them refurbishing weapons and equipment. The Negroes are quite skilled in many facets, as the North is learning.

The downside of this new freedom is that multitudes of Negro families are being left behind without protection because of the mission and the time schedule they are on. Another problem is the army cannot feed this new migration of Negro soldiers. There are too many mouths to feed and many are dying as a result. They must travel underground to survive. The southern forces are slaughtering groups of Negroes. Some Negroes have taken their own lives. They choose to die as free people rather than be enslaved again or die by the hands of the southern soldier.

Sherman is very shrewd in his tactics of war. He has burned

towns to the ground. The southerners have done so as well, but these stories have not been publicized. They have done this so the northerners cannot utilize the resources. Sherman is instilling the greatest fear amongst the southerners than anyone can imagine. Some of the southerners are beginning to flee as well. I am being told that death is rampant all around, from Atlanta through the Carolinas. The southerners are brave but losing hope. They have a lack of resources. It appears that Sherman and other generals are taking this war personally. It is rumored that a few of the northern generals have slaves themselves and really do not favor the Negro.

A lot of the wealthy have already invested their money up North and abroad. They have made alliances with family members and businesses in the North. They continue to spend large sums in my saloon. Their arrogance does not allow them to change their life-styles or status in this region. They try to show no fear or panic. Both sides are appropriating silver and gold to finance this war.

I have yet to be affected by these methods of financing. Thank God, they love my food and access to fine liquors. I somewhat have a monopoly on these delicacies of the rich, never revealing my means of acquisition. I am very discreet about my suppliers and it has paid off handsomely. They don't ask and I don't tell. Most dare not ask of my opinions on this civil unrest. A few have tried to pick my brain, but I have learned to dance around their inquisitions. I have yet to be cut off from the suppliers needed to maintain my business.

I knew the Civil War was coming before the first cannon was fired. At my establishment, through my prestigious clientele, I was privy to all of this information. It was revealed while sipping champagne and cognac. With this knowledge, I began to hoard liquors and cigars. I have learned to can a lot of produce so it will remain fresh and savory to the taste. This is one of the reasons I am so well known. The food still tastes like it is fresh from the harvest. The patrons wonder how this can be when so many crops have been pilfered and burned. I have a well-hidden place for my surplus that no one knows about.

Sherman has been so close that I can smell the smoke of death and hear the Archangel Michael blowing his horn! I fear not for my safety but the safety of those close to me. I do fear that in the event of my demise, my assets will not be discovered by my family or will fall into the hands of those not included in my will. I have provided information to family and a couple of others, with instructions, like pieces of a puzzle, to find my wealth in the event of my death, but not one person has all the pieces. I have also made other provisions for my family's well-being.

Many southerners are on both sides of the fence. Their loyalty is only beholden to their wealth and bloodline. I am known as one of the richest Negroes in the South, but I only show my wealth in the security of my establishment and my private domicile, which few are privy to. I have way greater means than that of which I declare. I have learned to hide assets. I constantly put money into my establishment by adding the newest and finest modern amenities so it appears that my profit goes right back into my business. Just as Sherman is shrewd in war, so am I in business. I would make a great general! I am the general of my own war. Only the Lord knows how much I have had to strategize to maintain neutrality. I constantly provide the community with turkeys, clothing, and books, which is illegal. I am always thinking. I need to find more time for private thoughts. These writings, this journal provides my sanity.

I would love to write a book, but I know too many secrets and it would not be allowed to be published. Maybe that is why this young man comes to me in dreams, seeking information as though he is interviewing me for a biography, or maybe it is just wishful thinking. Sometimes the comments he makes to me make me believe he already knows much about me. I feel a deep genetic relation to him. His heart is pure. There is love and concern in his presence. Is it a dream? At times, I wonder if he comes to me in a weary state of mind, in between consciousness and reality. It seems I am awake when he is present. When he leaves my thoughts, I am so rested, mentally and physically. Is this person really me in some other time or is it just my conscience laboring to the beyond when I am awake? I will not rationalize his existence too much so as not to jeopardize our relationship. I will not question this peace he gives me. There I go drifting away with thoughts again. I must be tiring or reaching another level of consciousness.

NO TIME TO HATE

A union brigade is near, sending many scouts through Augusta. There are spies among us from both sides. It is a known fact that the most prominent men of our time could be present in Augusta. It seems as if Augusta has remained neutral. I believe it is because of my good cooking, fine cigars, and liquors that Sherman will be coming back here to celebrate in the event of victory. It is hard to tell now who is who in my place. There are a lot of new faces that appear to be clandestine in nature. I stay away from their intense conversations and sometimes confrontations. I do not care to know these plots. I am not naive and I hear bits and pieces of their strategies. They usually occupy my private parlors. They appear to have bodyguards, even though no one is in military attire. I can tell by their intensity and mannerisms that they are regimented for one of the causes. I hear southern accents as well as northern speech communing together.

There is a bigger picture to this war, beyond what the mind could fathom. The information that I gather leads to the actions I have taken to preserve my wealth and family heritage. I see their two sides meet and discuss their secrets somewhat amicably over a fine meal and spirits, which makes me wonder why this war can't be settled over one of my finest meals, cigars, and cognac. Maybe this is what is occurring. I can tell that the parties that I speak of on both sides are of means. When they part ways, it is with a handshake and most of the time they procure my liquor and cigars, which they gift to each other. If they have nothing else in common, I do know they share the same fondness of my place.

I know that my place has been an integral part of this civil unrest. Maybe Sherman and Lee are already here in disguise. Well, time to say good morning again, Journal. Until we meet again, hopefully, prayerfully... My cigar has burned out!

Once again, Journal, I bid you good morning.

CHAPTER 12
STRENGTH IN MY TEARS

Dear Journal,
It is becoming difficult for me to get to my hidden place of treasures. Both sides are so close that they can see each other's campfires. This war brings very strange circumstances at times. My brother, Charles, thought of leaving Augusta and returning to the family in South Carolina. Boy, am I relieved that he stayed by my side. Sherman is running through Georgia and South Carolina like croppies and bass running up and down the Savannah River. I wish I could catch some red snapper in that river and some other fish that I serve on my menu. I have had to become very creative with my menu due to limited resources.

I really don't understand, at times, the strategies of either side and I wonder if they are confused. It appears that some generals fight for their cause, while others fight for their own benefit of glory and wealth. What I do see, though, is the destruction of such great properties. The southerners are getting very desperate for supplies. The blue coats have cut off many routes for them to unite in force. I guess conquer and divide. Many Augustans fear an invasion and an all-out battle. It appears that the northerners are using the Savannah River to their utmost advantage. They have cut off the waterways of this region. They have defeated the fort on the coast. It appears that the Union is the one on the offense, even though the southerners have made great stands against them, only to be defeated. It is ironic, though, how the money that was invested into the North by the southerners is now being used against them. They have forced the rebels to stay close to the coasts. Many await ships to take an excursion from this madness.

People that once dined, drank, and smoked fine cigars together are now enemies. Could there have been a better way to settle this indifference? I suggest a billiard tournament or drinking cognac until the last man stands. Too many egos are involved in this war. I guess I don't see the real picture. Remember, Journal, I have been in the middle of both sides and have heard the rationale of both. War should have been the last resort.

I suspect there will be wars until the end of time, as stated in the Bible. It is sometimes about economics or, at times, honor. No one is willing to compromise their way of life or beliefs. All can be respected as long as it doesn't call for the annihilation of a race or belief. I thought freedom of beliefs is what this country is supposed to be about.

This great land in which we live has plenty for all. Nobody wants to change. Without change, there is no progress. I believe that without change you begin to regress. History has proven that. Had I not been able to constantly change and broaden my menu, I would never have survived and prospered. You have to be willing to sample the new item on the menu; you may like it. We are so easily set in our ways and traditions. Change does not alter your heritage. No one can ever change that!

They say many concerns are that of profit. They are so far from the truth. I have had great cultures share each other's cuisines from the same plate without a second thought. It was part of my dream when I went into business to bond people with common tastes for life and to share with them a taste of Eden without the serpent.

It truly saddens me to be in the midst of civil unrest. I wish I were in a position to express my philosophy. I plant seeds in many great minds in my establishment, but they must be watered. Many seeds of peace are planted, but it is easier to destroy the crop. No one wants to work the land.

———————

I weep at night alone in my room
So many tears, so many fears that I cannot show
No one would understand the strength in my tears,
so I cry alone
I look to the sky and ask why did so many have to
die to be free
I know, dear Lord, that You have it all planned
But I still don't understand why so many have died
in this land
There is strength in my tears

CHAPTER 13
A NEW ERA POST-CIVIL WAR

Dear Journal,

Outside agitators are trying to disrupt our community. The same old money is in rule here, but it has been divested, along with others from the South who do not have the same beliefs of existing in harmony. If it were not for the northern investors, Augusta would be in a state of turmoil, a civil war within a city. We still would have our diehard rebels who believe a new war can be won. They have enlisted a southern militia that brings terror amongst the Negro and their sympathizers, but the Negro is so intertwined in the way of life here in Augusta. The southern whites are somewhat divided in their loyalty to the cause. It is a time of reconstruction and restructuring. The wise businessman has learned to diversify with the unification of new states and their beliefs in order to survive. I agree with this. I believe that in order to preserve the South, we have to become economically viable. Many were left with unusable, worthless confederate notes, their lands pilfered and decimated, thanks to Sherman and others.

The northerners have provided resources to rebirth the South. Some southerners' pride will not allow them to accept, as they feel, these handouts. Many southerners have moved west, leaving legacies behind. The Negroes have wised up, to a degree, and purchased vast amounts of land, which most were forced to flee by the militia. Some of the plantation owners have bequeathed their land to the Negro. The militia has many tactics for deterring the Negro from profiting from their loss. They will wait until a full crop has emerged and burn it to the ground. It is rumored that the Negro is following suit and doing the same to the white's crops. As a result, we are ending up with a barren land and no profits. They are cutting off their noses to spite their faces. Negroes who were sharecropping are migrating to the North for factory jobs. In the meantime, the white land owners have no one to sharecrop. Pride can make you starve. The three P's: pride, principles, and prejudice have ended many a nation. I have put my money into my business, oil, tobacco, railroads, rice, and exports. The three P's are limiting my exports. The sensible way is to put the three P's away and concentrate on the one big P (profit), then come back another day to fight.

It seems more lynching is occurring now that the Negro is free than before their emancipation. The whites had profited and were able to previously control the Negro without mass lynching. So much anger is involved now as the result of defeat. Just the thought of having a Negro look them straight in their eyes enrages them. The sad part is that it's not the plantation owners who are doing these malicious acts. The ones that are doing it don't own much, but the landowners can't go against the ungodly acts committed by these Europeans of questionable descent. If they did, they would be considered nigger lovers and their properties would surely be destroyed. Most of the people committing these atrocities were considered poor white trash before their rise to power. They were treated like slaves themselves, free by definition only. They were beholden to the plantation owner, lock, stock, and barrel, as the expression goes. So now they seek opportunity and revenge, compensation from both races. In effect, becoming abominations to their own race. They then try to place all the blame on the Negro for the death of the South. The northerners working around these areas of dysfunction are relaying a message of instability to investors. They are having to bring in law enforcement from government agencies to protect their investments and their safety.

CHAPTER 14
CIVIL RIGHTS

An article titled "Civil Rights" in *The Augusta Chronicle*, reads as follows:

A party of Negroes try to play the dodge on a colored barkeeper, but are failed.

Last evening, at about nine o'clock, a party of ten Negroes, headed by Richmond Hale (alias Miller), called on the saloon of Lexius Henson, colored, on Ellis Street and asked for drinks. Lexius told them at once that the saloon was a white man's bar and they ought not try to injure his business in that way. His scale of prices, he said, was as follows: beer $1 per glass, whiskey $2.50 per drink, brandy $5 per drink. The darkies, after some little chin music, left the saloon and retired to the corner of Ellis and McIntosh Street, where they engaged in earnest conversation. Finally, after a lengthy consultation, two of the men returned to the saloon, put two dollars on the counter, and called for two glasses of beer (it might have been all they could afford). Lexius peremptorily refused to serve them. They then left, *muttering something about five hundred dollars and making a new suit of clothes. Henson didn't seem a bit frightened by the threats.*

———————

Dear Journal,

Now, the whole purpose of my actions was for the New Reconstruction Civil Rights Laws. The law states that a business could be fined up to five hundred dollars for refusal of service to a Negro or non-white person. The part that has enraged me is that mine is the first establishment they've tried in Augusta. Now mind you, there are limited businesses like mine that are owned by Negroes, but this is still no cause to experiment with the new law on a colored man. Why didn't they have the courage to try this on a white establishment, to whom the law was targeted? I know that I am not liked by most of the Negro community, and I have been called many names: godless man, wannabe, white man by day and black man by night. As I have mentioned, Journal, we can and will be our own worst enemies until we learn to unite, regardless of the different shades of our race. They are falling right into the hands of the master's plan, and I use the term literally. This way of thinking must not occur, or we are doomed as a people for many years to come. We also need to learn that our character, skills, and education are the keys to acceptance, unity, and equality in society. W.E.B DuBois, Frederick Douglass, and Booker T. Washington all speak of the same mindset. We must first be recognized as humans, rational and functional beings in society, southern or northern. We must make a foothold in this direction.

I guess Mr. Hale and the others probably deemed this move as their rational approach to the beginning of a civil movement, but I cannot see how much thought it took for them to try me first. Maybe it was well contemplated amongst their group, but I do not see the logic. Maybe I am biased or limited in thought because I feel that I am also the victim. As they approached my business, I was in the back of the restaurant. I had already been forewarned minutes before of what was about to occur. I have eyes and ears all around Augusta and this region. Part of the key to my success is having these very important allies. I did not think those men would muster up the nerve to follow through on their plan. At the time, some important figures were present at my place. Maybe that is why they chose that time, because officials were present who were part of enforcing the new laws. I thought, at first, to question their presence; were they there by coincidence or part of this plan? So many thoughts were running through my head, so I played it by ear and sight. I closely watched the body movements of the possible conspirators. A little ruckus occurred and the officials silently came to my defense. We had to escort these men from the premises. It was a soft action, as I am accustomed to having to remove intoxicated or uncouth patrons. These men were sober and clear of mind. I have a couple of barrels of steel and buckshot to assist me and another loaded with corn kernels to cause severe scratches.

The Negro men went up the street and talked for a while. The sheriff eventually passed by with some coarse instructions because a crowd had begun to gather. Once the crowd dispersed, the original group remained. Two of them reentered and placed money on the bar. With my double-barrel friend beside me, the only friend I knew I could truly rely on, I refused them again and they left. Under their breath, they threatened to burn the place to the ground and put me in a coffin. Death I do not fear, but fire to my place, I do. I will never really know if this was strategically planned amongst parties with their own agenda.

CHAPTER 15
A GODLESS MAN

Dear Journal,
I have started my own church, rather God's church, called Springhill. Union Baptist has denied my membership because of the nature of my business, serving alcohol and having whites-only patrons. I have invested money into a new building and the care taking of a new minister and his family. He has recently moved to this town. I did not start a church out of spite or a desire to show my greatness, power, or stubbornness. I started it because I have a need for it in my life, I also started it for those who want to worship without pretenses. I am called a godless man by some, but not when they accept my turkeys at Thanksgiving and Christmas and the stocking fillers I provide. I do these things because it is the right thing to do. Yes, it makes me feel good inside. No, it is not done to equalize guilt, as some have stated. A godless person would not feel an inner peace as I do when I render what I call a show of love, but I have learned that you cannot please everyone. Pleasure radiates from within. I have changed the quality of many lives. In fact, when I retire at night, I ask myself, "Have I made myself a better man and

have I done something to help better someone else?" That is how I gauge my life. So if that is a godless man, then that is what I am!

Well, Journal, I have to make sure everything is in order before I retire … Until we meet again.

CHAPTER 16
LEXIUS JR.

Dear Journal,
I sit not far from my son, Lexius Jr. I watch as he peacefully sleeps. He is in one of the finest cribs a child can have. I have been told that I am tight on a dollar, but I spare no expense when it comes to my family and business. I will not force Lexius Jr. into my trade, my way of earning a living, but I will make it a point that he learns my culinary secrets and business ethics. As he comes of age, I am sure he will be the best at what he does and will shine through. I will make sure that all options will be placed at his disposal. He is such a handsome child, a little man. I believe him to favor myself. He is of my complexion and it does not appear that his hair texture or skin color will change. It would not matter if either would, Journal, it is just an observation. Lexius Jr. came into the world with his eyes wide open, which is rare. He was quite alert; no need to spank his bottom. All I could say was, "That's my boy!" A chip off the old block. I constantly wonder how his life will be. It is a good thing, not an obsession, but I have been told that it is a natural reflex to child rearing.

He has helped me take time out to think about other things besides my restaurant and business. At the same time, it has motivated me to be more productive in every capacity of my life: spiritually, monetarily, etc. I look at Lexius Jr. and I am inspired to have at least one more child. I must find time to be a father. My father had so many children and a profession as a physician that was very demanding. My father was a very loving man, though his time to spend with family was limited. I would love to have many children, but I do not want to deprive them of me. I must pass on a legitimate legacy. Character and morals are everything. Like I said, he does not have to duplicate my business or goals, but I do wish to instill my passion and mindset to Lexius Jr.

What a beautiful man child. He has a grip that could swing a mean cleaver or a wood chopping axe. They say he is moving too fast already, which means he is making room for another sibling to come along. I am all for that. It is a most auspicious time to bring a child into this world, during this historical period. He is a healthy, plump little fellow, with curly hair and fat, rosy chicks. His health is well. I check on him constantly when I am around, placing my hand on his chest as it rises with a breath of fresh air. The first five years are the most challenging for children's survival. Lexius Jr. has gotten off to a good start.

I believe when I look at Lexius Jr., he gives me such a peace of mind that overwhelms my soul. At the same time, I have anxiety, with the deepest concerns about the state of the world now and to come. But I have strong faith that God has chosen to bring me this child at this time. My wife is well after a long labor. How did she ever birth this ten-pound turkey? The baby was quite long as well. So was I, I am told. Oh, my goodness, does he have an appetite! He was born with two teeth. The nipple is not going to suffice his need for nourishment. We started him young on mashed potatoes and well-chewed food. Breast milk was just not satisfying Master Lexius Jr. He has good, strong Henson genes. There is no doubt of heritage. All of the Henson features are present. Will he go on to bear children? How will they turn out? What kind of father will he become? I guess that will be determined by what kind of father I will be to him. I strongly believe this is a major contributing factor in how future generations progress.

I believe the genes primarily dictate one's character, but I also believe that a life can be altered by his or her environment. I truly believe that genes will ultimately prevail and supersede any environmental regime. The Assyrians believe this logic as well. My job will be to try and make life easier so my child will not have to experiment with theories and laws of existence that have yet to be proven.

I know I cannot always isolate all factors for the term of Lexius Jr.'s stay under my roof, but I can eliminate some of the odds. Life can be a gamble, but don't play a game with bad odds or a game you know you cannot win. Lexius Henson Jr. was born into a game that he can win because God and I are his dealers. Many children are not given the luxury of such options, the proverbial "silver spoon." I have a restaurant full of silver spoons.

Journal, I have missed many days talking to you. There's a lot on my plate. Fortunately, the peace that I receive from my child supplements the relationship I have with you. I will teach Lexius Jr. the strength of having a friend such as you, Journal.

Son, I love you so much, beyond belief. Every time I look at you, it brings a smile to my face and joy to my heart, total elation. A greater feeling than any piece of gold. Thank you, my wife, for allowing yourself to become the vessel of such a valuable, priceless gift. No other possession that I own can compare to that which you have shared with me. I cannot articulate the jubilation that has overwhelmed me. It is my practice not to owe any man or woman, only God; however, I find myself indebted to you, Edwina, my beautiful wife, forever.

Many say I have a new glow about myself. I, too, see it and embrace it. The glow gives me such warmth, far greater than the finest blanket or quilt I possess. I vow to you, my wife and child, that I will be your comforter. I promise to you my life and I give to you both abundantly and without pretense. All praise to the Most High beyond the skies, who created heaven and earth. Lexius Jr. and my wife, sleep well. Journal, until we meet again. Good morning, because daylight approaches.

P.S. Call me, Journal. I hear you when you beckon for my ink.

CHAPTER 17
A New Year

Dear Journal,

Another year has come and gone; they seem to go by faster each year. I delivered more than eighty turkeys this year for Christmas. I gave out 150 pounds of yams and made about 200 pounds of stuffing. We made over one hundred pies, mostly sweet potato and pumpkin. The list gets longer each year, with new families to feed. I receive much pleasure in delivering these gifts. I wish I could do it more often than just at Thanksgiving and Christmas. I help throughout the year, but not in the numbers I wish I could do. They are definitely gifts from the heart. Many sneer at me in the background as I pass out these turkeys. I will still be disliked amongst my people. I will always consider them my people, even though it is often not reciprocated, a lot of times, because of the ignorance of not knowing the man I really am and what I believe in. My father taught me long ago that you cannot and will not be able to make everyone happy. It really used to bother me much more, even though I was taught to be prepared for this. I still have moments of despair on this matter.

There will always be haves and have nots. I happen to be one of the haves. I guess you could say a silver spoon dished life out to me, but most of the silver was from the silver-tongued man of wisdom, my father. Yes, my father was a doctor, but he made wise choices in life. He gave away much wisdom and help to those who could not afford his practice. He was not only a healer of men, but a healer of souls. He believed in higher education at any expense, even if it meant long hours of studying before or after doing chores.

My brother, Charles, and I could very well have followed in our father's footsteps.

He used to tell us there were easier ways to make money, but there were no shortcuts. We were encouraged to leave the nest, so we ventured out to new lands and opportunities. We used to take leisure trips to Augusta and found it to be a pleasing environment to which we were accustomed. The races got along well and everyone knew their place. There weren't many interracial relationships and marriages when I first moved to Augusta, which I was accustomed to in South Carolina. In Augusta, it is illegal to marry outside of your race, whereas it was legal in South Carolina. What has occurred here in Augusta and the majority of the South is a creation of a new race called mulattos. White men of Irish, British, and Welsh descent are marrying who they believe to be women of one hundred percent European descent as well. Some knowingly marry mulattos who could pass for one hundred percent European. Some of them are united with those from the most elite backgrounds. Most people of higher means research family backgrounds before they wed. We, as mulattos, have taken a silent oath not to reveal another mulatto who has chosen to pass as full European. There are more of these people than you would think.

Generations to come will never know they are of African descent, along with other nationalities they are not supposed to wed, let alone bear children. Eventually, we will all be related. The mulatto gene started from abroad and by generations passed, one would never know. Money still married money. I am classified as Negro, even though I am of Irish, British, Welsh, African, and American Indian descent. Some records show me as Negro, while others state that I am a mulatto. We mulattos are often of great financial means, cultured, and of higher education.

There are those who would jump into the Savannah River with a rock tied around their necks if they knew who they were wedded to and seeded children with. It was okay for masters to sire children by slaves and walk around like peacocks while their wives and families had knowledge of the infidelity. This was the norm. But he would sooner put one in the chamber, hold it to his head, and die than give one of those children his name or birthright. The slaves took the plantation owners' last names, but this was a whole different cup of tea.

Well anyway, back to the holidays, Journal. Church was good. The new church is growing in membership. Overall, I think the Augusta community has had a prosperous Christmas and a good year. The new year appears to be leading to another good one. I continue to look for wise investments. Yes, there is such a thing in these times, and I have the inside information on the correct choices to make from the wealthiest men. Well, I have to get up early to take in the beginning of the new monthly stock. It will be a long day.

Journal, until we meet again, I bid you a happy New Year and a good morning!

CHAPTER 18
LITIGATION

Dear Journal,
    I am being sued for monies for an alleged breach of contract. Simply put, a shyster is trying to make commission on the sale of a property that he had no dealings with. I was approached by an agency when I was going to purchase the *Augusta Chronicle* building. This agency was to represent the seller in the procurement of this property.

Mind you, there were no contracts signed on this matter. My attorney has been out of town on another business matter, but he and I are in contact. I have been told by a reliable source that the acting agent had raised the price to better his commission. I was originally given a lower price. Then the so-called agent approached me to serve as a broker. I told him if he could negotiate a good deal, I would allow him to represent the deal on my behalf. Once again, no contracts were signed. I did agree to a commission if he negotiated a price that was of interest to my attorney and me. I had set the price to what I was willing to pay.

The price he had presented was much higher, and after consulting with my attorney, we deemed the price to be too high. At no time did I give the agent sole negotiating power of attorney. I told him I was well abreast on negotiating these types of deals on my own and I had my own counsel, but if he could get a better deal, he would be compensated; this never occurred. He was out to make a buck on me. He should have known that I had a reputation for being a shrewd businessman and a very wise negotiator. Come to find out, the reputable company that he was supposedly representing did not know he was a part of this sale.

He was trying to make money on the side. The company he worked for was a fair company. As soon as I found out he was misrepresenting his company and myself, I discontinued conversation with him and continued to negotiate on my own. I ended up purchasing the property for much less than the crooked agent attempted to fleece. After the deal was signed, sealed, and delivered, he approached me for a commission without the knowledge that I had already uncovered his scandal. I asked whether he was intoxicated or smoking opium. He said if it were not for his negotiations with the seller, the price would never have been lowered. Of course, I know this was a lie because I had personally negotiated with the seller. The seller had also made me aware of his motives. The businessmen in this community look out for each other. I am hearing now that outside sources were trying to purchase this property in order to operate the same type of business I operate. My sources say the agent was being paid to corrupt the deal and make me lose money so I would not be able to expand my business. I told him I would see him in court.

———

Court did not go well. It is obvious that some hands were greased with bribes. The agent produced contracts that allegedly had my signature. I have a unique signature. A patron of great wealth taught me not to have an easily duplicated signature because it would make me vulnerable to thieves. He said that is what the wealthy do. I had wondered in my early years why my patrons of great means had illegible signatures. I thought they were not educated, at least in penmanship. I was also taught to secure my documents under lock and key and not to be so quick to sign my name without a witness. As of now, what I had been taught is not helping due to the corruption in the courts. My attorney says not to worry; we can get this matter moved to another court.

———

It is day three, and the judge can't make a ruling. My prominent attorney has connections. He has pressured the judge to pass this case to a higher court. This way, the judge still gets his payoff and stays in good standing with the scheming coup and there will not be a division amongst the local community.

It was starting to become an issue of divide in the district. It was slightly affecting my clientele. But one thing is for certain: My recipes kept everyone on common ground. A meal at my place or a fine cigar and cocktail cannot be compromised. Many disputes are settled at my establishment because of the ambiance I provide. Many have come in angry, but few leave unhappy. Hey, I like that slogan, Journal. I must make a note to use that on fliers, newspaper advertisements, etc. Guess what, Journal, what is done in the dark always comes to light.

I overheard a man who was part of the coup tell another man that even if he was able to purchase the building, he would, in no way, be able to duplicate the quality of my place. It is much more desirable to be a patron than the owner of this place. The patron I'd overheard is not the one suing me, though. The individual agent has filed suit. He has lost his job for misrepresenting the company he worked for. The backer of this initial scandal has gone on about his business and has left this agent, I have been told, without compensation. They found out that I was not one to trifle with and my connections were strong as well. Being a Judas is a tough life, I guess. The agent knows that he can't go after the wealthier initiator of the coup, so he figures I do not have the resources, connections, or knowledge to prevail in court. Guess what, Journal, I am well stocked in all of those categories. His co-conspirators love my place now. Keep the faith and do right by other people, and God will help you prevail. People say that I am godless, but once again, this is far from the truth. I am in His favor. The agent's followers are dwindling by the day, but the case is not yet won. I shouldn't count my chickens yet.

———————

The case has been moved to the Supreme Court of Georgia. I was taught to always put away money for legal matters when in business because someone is going to try and take it for one reason or another. Laws are changing rapidly in this era. I make it a point to be current on all legislature, past, present, and the ones discussed for the future. I love to read, history and law being my favorite. I thought of becoming an attorney or a teacher of history at one point in my life. I am like a general in war. Know your enemy's history. Know his journey and his motivation, or lack thereof. Many wars have been won by following another man's battle, his journey to the war and during.

I have no worries because once the case reaches the Supreme Court, it can be a swift judgment or a long wait. The agent's case is very weak. His strength was in the alliance of his backers and the judge, and both have abandoned their alliance. The signature will easily be proven to be fraudulent. I have recovered important documents to prove the signature to be counterfeit. The agent never thought this matter would leave the local level of law and I believe he did not spend quality time forging the documents.

———————

Things are back to normal at my establishment and my case is not an everyday cocktail conversation. All sides are back together, even though they still never missed a meal at my place. I find humor in the fact that the people betting against me still partake in my cooking. They should be very grateful that I don't mix vengeance with my recipes.

The agent was unable to discredit my reputation; so I'd won the main battle. In the event the Supreme Court rules against me, I have the money in escrow. His commission would not have been that immense, which alerted me to the fact that there had to be other motivating factors behind this lawsuit. I have always learned to look beyond the surface of what man says. "Man speaketh with a forked tongue." Very few are articulate enough to state what they really mean.

In my business, I serve as counsel, therapist, and healer of souls. I have a different awareness than most, a third eye, so to speak. That is what I have named it. Rumors are that this agent relocated to another county. Remember, he was never paid by the conspirators and he has lost his reputable representation. It's time for him to change occupations. He is lucky I didn't have him tarred and feathered and run out of town. The suggestion was placed at my disposal by some of my patrons. I ended up doing business with some of his conspirators.

A decision was handed down from the Supreme Court, a unanimous vote against the complainant. My relationship with the conspirators became a very profitable one that formed many ventures. Not only did they love my food, they loved my strength and knowledge as a warrior and a strong businessman. Respect is one of the most important and priceless values of our times.

I can see where new money in our society will change the course of what old money represented. New money knows no order or class, just profit. In order to maintain a congenial existence, I believe the principles of old money must persevere or economical balance will become jeopardized. I believe the rich want just a rich or poor status, but I think there will be some change in that mindset. The rich want old money to be dominant, but they also don't want people to be dirt poor, because these people will revolt and come after their riches eventually.

Those with new money don't care one way or the other because they are so engrossed in maintaining new wealth and attaining more. Old money will never dwindle; it is so deeply rooted. Five or so families and hierarchies rule the world's wealth. A southern man who has lost his wealth still has his dignity and self-worth. You can always detect when Old Money walks into a room by its manner-ism. He may not have a nickel in his pocket, but you would never know. New Money makes sure his entrance into a room doesn't go unnoticed and is just as quick to show how much money is in his purse. He usually asks, "How much is this going to cost me?" whereas Old Money just orders it. Like the saying goes, "If you have to ask how much it costs, you probably can't afford it."

The new money conspirator has tried to invest in oil and steel. Some have been lucky, digging wells and hitting gushes in the ground for immediate wealth. A lot of them foolishly lose their wealth as soon as they acquire it. Steel is a wise investment. Everything is being built with this resilient invention—trains need it, railroad tracks, those new high-rise structures. Almost all things of this day are being manufac-tured with this strong alloy. The strength and longevity of steel will make things last almost forever. It takes intense heat to form it into its many shapes and it takes an ever more intense heat to destroy it. Steel is creating great wealth for the nation.

One of the up-and-coming businesses is the railroad, used to transport people and goods across the land and to the seaports in an expeditious manner. Time for producing commerce has been reduced significantly. That is why my new and old money associates have given me insight on a new means of profit. I have already known of these new ventures from my old money patrons, but they are slow to show you the route to attain it. My new money associates are quick to show you, of which I take full advantage. This could also be their downfall because they are loose with their tongues. Journal, I am letting only you know of my new dealings. You are the only one I can trust.

Back to the case … The agent failed to prove that I had entered into any type of contract with him, written or oral, to share monies on a commission based on the sale of the property. Oh, happy day, Journal! This was a moral victory more so than a monetary one. It goes to show you, as I was trying to articulate, that old money will prevail. It is apparent that the old money Supreme Court saw through the ruse. The agent never produced any contracts with signatures and his felonious witnesses never surfaced. I do not gloat over the victory, but I am joyous, of course. I was almost the last to receive the good news. Some of my patrons have planned a celebration for me. It does not take much in Georgia for someone to have a reason to celebrate. The aristocrats here will celebrate even when it floods or because the sun rose and set today. I cannot turn down the invitation to have a gala on my behalf. And guess who is giving it, the one who conspired against me originally; it was his idea, to show how big of a man he is to accept his defeat. This should turn out to be a soiree to remember.

My patrons have compensated me to shut down my establishment for this event. All of the most prominent citizens will be present. They have also provided the menu, which is pretty much the same as what I already provide. I will still end up overseeing my own banquet. I guess it's the thought that counts. They actually want to dine with me.

Although I have been asked, on occasion, to sit and dine with them, I never mixed business with pleasure. There still is an order to be maintained. I cannot and will not cross that proverbial line. Interference from drunkenness may cause a permanent soberness for me, if you know what I mean, Journal. A new suit and someone standing over me, saying some words.

I have taken liberty in smoking a cigar very rarely so as not to insult my guests, but I would never dine with my patrons. My plan is pre-rehearsed, where my staff will bring me a non-alcoholic beverage, unbeknownst to my patrons, as they will be inebriated and easily fooled. I will allow them to toast me and continue to celebrate in my honor. I guess I have truly arrived. God is good! I have one of the finest restaurants in the country, and I am one of the richest men of color, but I come from a comfortable financial background and of education. I consider myself old money as well; therefore, I cannot celebrate with my patrons like this is the event of my life.

It is business as usual. To be successful, you must be accustomed to adversity. I cannot offend them by declining. They are actually celebrating a victory for themselves, that I took on New Money and was victorious, a testing ground. I stopped New Money, literally, in its tracks, showing them that it takes more than new wealth to prevail over southern ways. Old Money was riding the fence as to which side it was on. But I found that Old Money was my ally when the lawsuit reached the Supreme Court. They are very appreciative of my victory. It was, as we call it, "testing the waters" for new shysters trying to capitalize on our southern complacencies.

I will order some amenities that I normally would not. Remember, I am a businessman of opportunity as well. I will let them sponsor a great deal of my monthly income, in essence, without a month of overhead. What I will do is block off a floor and let family and friends enjoy the fruits of my victory, which is their victory as well.

Oh, by the way, I have recently discovered that the agent has disappeared, not relocated. I inquire not; it is not my business to know his whereabouts.

A journey means a beginning of new discovery, maybe without an ending, but with great effort, seeking an ending. Without a journey, you just exist.

Dear Journal, until we meet again. I bid you a good morning.

CHAPTER 19
FINE DINING

Dear Journal,
I have set a very high standard in my business; that is why I attract the elite. Those who have been to upstate restaurants appreciate my elegance. Those who are well to do but have not had the pleasure of traveling upstate or abroad are able to experience these royalties through my establishment.

Perfection is a must, and I sometimes have tantrums with my staff to maintain the best that the South, or North, or anyone can offer. This intense focus on efficiency and perfection relaxes me. I guess it makes me feel that I have used my mind and it gives me a feeling of accomplishment for that day. I try to teach people who are trying to better themselves to always have a checklist at the beginning and end of the day.

My restaurant is of private membership, even though I accommodate the public on a couple of my floors. The cigar, oyster bar, and billiards are open to the public and restricted to whites only. I do, on special occasions, allow weddings and other social events for the Negros, very discreetly, though. My other patrons would not appreciate sharing their socially elite Eden with someone of a lesser class and race. If they knew that my silverware had touched the tongues of Negroes, they would chop off the tongues of both theirs and the Negroes'.

I set my prices high to minimize my clientele. Some save for months to splurge at my place, but these people are looked down upon by my old money patrons. It is amazing that no matter the color, there will be separation amongst all races, especially when it comes to the dollar.

Many of my old money clientele will not turn down new money business ventures or Negro money ventures, but still will not give passage or an invitation to their palatial estates. Old Money will go broke before it associates with New Money. This motivates New Money to reach higher wealth out of spite.

The economy in this region is good, with all the mills, cotton, rice, turpentine, coal mines, and import and export. The resources are so vast and diversified that I can never see them being exhausted.

I do not know if my investments will be passed on to generations to come. It is questionable as to whether my bloodline will still exist. Many of my family have already disappeared into other lives and identities. The Europeans' bloodlines will be altered for generations to come. They have put a halt to interracial breeding, but they, too, have spotted lineage; they are unable to hide such scars. A lot of them have multiple families and obligations. I see a day when there will be a race called the rainbow race. I still truly believe we are all from the same seed and sometimes the wind blows the seeds on to other grounds.

Those children of discreet relations are usually given means to move elsewhere and start new lives without heritage. Some take on the role of Europeans, while others find communities of their same makeup. One thing I know for sure is that Old Money will always be in rule. My relative from another time reveals to me that my deductions are quite accurate.

One of my patrons caught his wife with one of his business partners slipping out of the backyard today. The irony of this is that my patron was having relations with his partner's wife and mistress as well. I don't know which one started the infidelity, but I could not have this scandal out in the open at my place. Both spouses were not of beauty, Journal, so I tend to believe their actions were out of spite and dislike for each other or one of those nights of intoxication. The grape can be very evil if you allow it to be. You could not have paid me all the tea in China to be with any of the three women. I guess the grape brings the beauty out of the beast.

I take humor in these fracases because I am usually highly compensated to keep these incidents out of the *Augusta Chronicle*. It is hilarious to me that this elite group of people are raising each other's children and are of relation, and I am the only one other than their wives who know their true family lineage. Maybe that is why they continue to allow me to be prosperous.

The rule of my place is that what happens here stays here. My staff has had to escort some patrons home. In some cases, my Negro staff would be hung from the highest tree for the measures they have taken to restore order. To date, there has been only one attempt at retaliation against my staff for maintaining the peace. It involved a new money patron. We nipped that right in the bud with the sheriff. One of the families on my staff had to flee north because the wife involved in this incident was sober enough to remember how the staff had removed her from the premises. To take the focus off of her, she gave great detail as to how the Negro had accosted her and her husband and stated to some of her new money friends that she needed retribution for the disrespect. To restore her honor, rumor of a hanging came across my feet. The sheriff gave warning to the hanging party to leave the matter alone. I financed and arranged the relocation of one of my most valued staff members and his family. I could not give an opinion on the disciplinary action that was to be taken because it would mean acknowledging that I had sanctioned this activity as the wife had implied.

She came to an untimely demise along with her lover. Her lover's death occurred while on a fishing trip and hers, we assumed, came shortly after her disappearance. Neither of the bodies were ever found. There are a lot of stories about mysterious deaths in the South; they are usually related to infidelity. She should have left well enough alone. She had married Old Money by trickery, so the embarrassment had to be erased.

I wish I were able to write a book about the goings on at my gentlemen's and ladies restaurant. It would be a diary of my demise. I do fear at times, though, that my knowledge of these elite people's secrets will be the cause of my death. I do not hold any of these secrets over my clients' heads and they do appreciate that. Most of the time, they ask me what happened and I respond, "What happened?" I believe I am not a threat to their status, but I always keep a watchful eye and don't venture too far from my fortress without security in place.

Well, I guess I'll have a warm glass of milk with my usual sedative. I don't have the luxury to partake in the grape throughout the day, which is a good thing because I cannot afford distractions. I have observed my patrons of power make many bad choices under the influence of alcohol, which has affected the outcome of our future.

I have benefited from their inebriation and learned to manipulate things to my advantage, but nothing immoral. They will sign anything while in this state of mind and they will not renege upon the agreement that we've made. Mind you, I never instigate or initiate any of these dealings and ask them at least twice if they are sure of what they are saying and signing. They get somewhat indignant if you question them, so I go with the flow. They will always honor the agreement so as not to admit to their transgressions while under the influence of the grape. Honor and integrity are everything to a southern gentleman. Yes, you can say I am shrewd, Journal, but I have been educated by the shrewdest.

Good morning, Journal. Until we meet again.

CHAPTER 20
TEMPTATION

Dear Journal,
I will never admit infidelity to you, my journal, but infidelity can exist in the thoughts. I will never leave a legacy of negativity, never mix business with pleasure. The pleasure is in the business. I have been propositioned on literally hundreds of occasions. This is why I stay away from the fermented grape. I am told that I am a very handsome man by women other than my wife. I am already classified as a heathen and a man of ungodly spirit just because I serve alcohol at my establishment. I have closed my eyes to the opportunities of the devil. I will leave you with that.

If I did succumb to the temptation, I know that would be the death of me. I continually warn John Hope and a fellow employee of the consequences of allowing their egos to rule their courses of action while escorting patrons home. I do not inquire about the events of the journey. I know personally that it takes the strength of a Greek warrior to turn down advances by these patrons. The husbands send their wives home so they may play, not thinking that their wives have the same thoughts of infidelity dancing through their corsets. A lot of times, spite is the woman's justification. Once again, Journal, I am just speculating.

CHAPTER 21
MEMORIAL DAY

Dear Journal,
One of my favorite times of the year has come, Memorial Day. It is a time to celebrate the lives of the people who have come to pass before me and the fact that life goes on. It is a time to appreciate the passing of those who were dear, a time to reflect on the future as well.

I've started roasting pigs and marinating my spare ribs. I have a pit dug into the ground where I place coal, soaked wood chips, and other secrets into the fire. I place the pigs on a steel grate and cover them with palm leaves. I have mastered the flame necessary to cook like an oven, slow but with enough heat to maintain a constant temperature. You have to be careful when cooking the swine so as not to poison it with uneven temperatures. I use many spices that I will not even entrust to you, Journal. Okay, a couple just to tease you: garlic, cinnamon, mustard, a citrus fruit, and brown sugar. That's more than enough secrets told. Of course, I have left out the keys to unlock the ultimate Henson cuisine. I cook it for about … Oops! I almost gave away another vital secret. Let's just say I start during the beginning of the evening, and I am done somewhere near noon the next day.

My cooks are trusted with the recipes and techniques and I make them swear an oath that they will never reveal the process. I have told them that I will bury them with the pig, like pharaohs did the slaves who had built the Great Pyramids, in order to keep the secrets concealed forever. They know all too well how serious I am about maintaining the secrets of my culinary skills.

I save my finest cigars for this occasion. The cigars are also used as a timer for my cooking, by the number of cigars I've smoked—another mystery. The meat literally falls off the bones. You could pull pork off the pig with your fingers. I have coined the term "pulled pork," which I serve loose or as a sandwich.

I have created and named many dishes, which many a fine chef have tried to duplicate. I probably will never receive the acclaim for the original dishes, but I will take all glory in knowing that I was the first to market it. I have a concoction that I use to marinate the pork and other meats that I cook. I will give a couple of the secrets once again. I hope this doesn't fall into the wrong hands! I use vinegar, beer, and spices mixed together. I will not reveal all of the spices; use your imagination. It is not necessary to marinate all meats over-night, as long as you marinate with the liquid as you cook. Okay, now I will have to burn you, Journal; you know too much.

I cook both pork and beef ribs and, on occasion, lamb and goat. I meticulously clean all the fat off the ribs, making sure I remove all the skin membrane. This is one of the keys to the savory pre-seasoned meat holding the spices, a very important part of the process. If you don't remove the fat and membrane, the seasoning rolls right off the meat as soon as the heat hits it. I never cook the ribs with the sauce on them, not even when I am smoking them at the end of cooking. I dip the meat into the sauce that is simmering on the stove after I pull it off the grate. It absorbs so much better. This is what makes the difference between my barbecue and other recipes used by my competitors. Let me correct that … I will be arrogant at this point; there is no competition or comparison to my ribs as a result of my techniques.

I bet any man that he cannot eat my ribs without letting out a moan and licking his fingers. You can eat my sauce without the meat; it is as succulent as the meat itself! Dip some white bread into it and, oh my goodness, it is a meal. I sell my sauce by the gallons. I have been offered a lot of money to market my sauce. Many have tried to duplicate it, but no one has been able to thus far. I am the king saucier!

This is one of the rare times when I get to invite family and friends to have a holiday. On these days, we play whist, dominoes, darts, Chinese checkers, poker, horseshoes, and croquet. These games become quite exciting and challenging and very competitive. Some still consider these games to be evil because back in the day they were outlawed, believe it or not, by the Queen's court, who had deemed them to be evil. The cards were equated to astrological signs, seasons, and other naive beliefs. The ace of spades actually symbolized that taxes had been paid for manufacturing of the cards. Some believe the twelve honors of the deck refer to the signs of the zodiac or the months of the year. They say the two colors refer to the solstice and equinox phases. They see the four suits as the seasons. The entire pack of fifty-two cards represent the weeks in a year. The faces of the kings were based on historical rule: Alexander the Great, the King of Clubs, the young Macedonian general who led his troops from Greece to India, wearing a costume embroidered with a lion; David, the King of Spades, the psalmist standing by a harp; Julius Caesar, the King of Diamonds, the dictator of Rome, with his robes displaying a Roman eagle; Charles the Great, the King of Hearts, Charlemagne, the founder of the Roman empire, carrying a globe. I have learned to research all that I do so the naysayers will not have a leg to stand on when they try to condemn my actions or lifestyle. I am quite the historian.

The moon is full tonight, to my delight. It seems the face of the moon smiles even greater at every hand that I run. My partner and I have mastered the game of whist. We talk across the table by using different anecdotes so both know what to play. The practice is banned if detected, but both sides do the same. It is all part of the game. We begin by being reserved in our play, but that does not last long. As soon as one team romps another, the war begins. It is such a relief, such a pleasure from my daily routine. I actually get to forget my obligations for a weekend.

We have a lot of delicacies at our disposal, almost to a point of gluttony. I do not spare any expense on this holiday. We partake in the grapes and ales but not to a point of drunkenness. It will be talked about amongst my inner circle for months, until we meet again. Those who are victorious in the games seem to never stop talking, bragging of their expertise. Many in the neighborhood talk about our holiday weekend as though we are heathens, but those who do so only wish they had been present. Usually a group will stay the weekend. I make all accommodations for their stay at no charge.

We live as kings and queens, like the faces of the cards we play. Even though it is supposed to be a holiday for remembrance of those gone, it rejuvenates life amongst us and gives us all a reprieve from our hectic lives. I so look forward to this holiday. We hate to depart from these days.

The man in the moon is still smiling at me and my guests and we are exuberantly smiling back at him. One of my guests swears that the moon tipped his hat at him. I think it is time to cut him off from the cognac. It is Saturday, one more morning rise to come. This is the only Sunday that I miss services. We don't go to sleep until morning rises. Some of my guests do not leave until Monday.

I always tease those who stay, claiming that at midnight on Monday, all lodging rates will be charged along with charges for all the amenities. We have a spectacular breakfast for those who can get up. We have fish and grits, pork steaks, eggs Benedict, omelets, imported kiwi, mangos, pineapple, quail, pheasant, sausages, bacon, croissants, biscuits, French bread, fresh butter, gravy, oranges, apples, grapefruit, papaya, banana, and zucchini bread. I am sure I have left some items off the menu.

I send my guests off with a nice picnic basket on Monday morning. We eat oysters, crabs, lobster, stripers, bass, yellow perch, catfish, offshore shark, mako, trout, red drum, and sunfish. We had turkey, wild boar, deer, snake, waterfowl, and crayfish. When I say we have a feast, I mean a feast.

My guests joke that they fast for a week prior to coming to this event just so they can gorge themselves. I also include some of the finest cigars. They joke about how cheap and tight I am on a normal day, so they take full advantage of my splurge. I do the same by treating myself, as I normally don't have the luxury.

Playing whist, horseshoes, and dominoes continue all night long. We celebrate on the roof and the back courtyard by torch light. I am the reigning champ of whist. I believe they honor the host sometimes with an easy victory, which I can't stand. I tell them not to patronize me, that I can whoop any of them while blindfolded. I threaten to cut them off from the festivities if they give me an easy victory.

I love competition in any form. It gives me a natural elation that no grape can provide. That is how mine has become one of the top restaurants in the South. I constantly add items to my menu along with other amenities. I do this in order to stay ahead of the pack. My guests say they need a week to recuperate from these two and a half days. I bounce right back because I am accustomed to no sleep and the adrenaline this holiday provides. I partake in the grape very sparingly, usually only for a special toast, but they will toast to even a firefly lighting up on this weekend. I do indulge in my cigars, though.

I prepare most of my food a couple of days prior to the guests' arrival so I can enjoy the festivities as well. My staff usually cooks the meat as I oversee the process. I have learned many ways to preserve freshness in my dishes so they taste as if they were just prepared.

My friend who said he'd seen the moon tip his hat dances and sings the entire weekend, even upon departure, possibly because he is one of the most popular entertainers in the region and he enjoys what he does. We also enjoy it thoroughly. You would think he would have a holiday from his profession, but I guess that is just his persona. Look who is talking; I am literally still doing the same thing I do every day also. I guess if it's in your blood, it's in your blood.

My patrons begged me not to close on this weekend, so I have come up with another means to supply them with my services by way of a catering staff. I am still making money while I entertain. I have turned my catering business over to the young John Hope and he manages it quite well. The main affair is at the private country club across the Savannah River. This is where most of the affluent southerners in and out of this district attend on this holiday. It is pretty much a duplication of my menu, but I do add a little extra to my menu to feel special, if you know what I mean.

CHAPTER 22
JOHN HOPE

Dear Journal,
  John Hope comes from a very fine family. His father died when he was still a lad. The inheritance that he was entitled to was not endowed to him or his family. His family comes from a very well-to-do background of Scottish descent. I catered to his father on many occasions; what a fine gentleman and scholar of unquestionable character. On one Christmas, his father invited some homeless gentlemen to a dinner of turkey and all the trimmings of which he and his wife had meticulously prepared, leaving his own family without food for the festive occasion. John's dad had contacted me and asked, along with an apology, whether I could provide a turkey and trimmings for his family for that day. I could only joyfully oblige that fine gentleman and his family, even if it meant the turkey from my own table; that is how high my regard was for him. It was very short notice when John and his father had showed up at my doorstep with this request, but by suppertime his feast was delivered. It was my total pleasure to be a part of that day.

  I give and don't tell. I've learned a lot from John Hope's father.

John has come to me for more money lately for his educational needs, but unfortunately, I could not increase his wages at this time. I have invested a lot of money into my new building, the old *Augusta Chronicle Newspaper* building, but I do supplement his income by other means. I put John Hope in a position of authority. He is compensated by patrons for catering and other things I have taught him to order and know: fine wines, liquor, cigars, and all of the fine things I offer at my restaurant. I have allowed him to subcontract himself out to the rich, for which he is handsomely rewarded. I know his expenses have increased, but I have taught him how to budget quite well. I ask for no percentage of the money from which he has profited as a result of my connections. It may appear, and I have heard, that I have been selfish towards him, but this is far from the truth.

John Hope has created quite a name for himself with the skills he has rendered to my clientele. He is such a perfectionist, as am I, and as I have taught him to be. I may never get the credit for mentoring this young protégé, but hopefully he knows the truth. I don't do it for the recognition. He is part of a legacy for me. My sons may not carry on this part of me. I love John Hope as a son, but it may seem that I don't show it that way. A lot of people say I am without heart, but they don't know me. I live better to enrich my soul spiritually as well as those around me.

I have taken John Hope under my wing and my tutelage as I would my own flesh. I consider him family and I would hope he feels the same way. The lessons I have shared with him are priceless. Not to mention, he can beat me in an occasional chess match, which is something that few can brag about. I always get on the subject of John Hope, Journal. This should say something about my feelings for him.

CHAPTER 23
MEMORIAL DAY CONTINUES

Dear Journal,
I have been sneaking away to log the Memorial Day events. I usually never mention it, but the days are growing old as well as myself. There are quite a few on the who's who list at my Memorial Day extravaganza, but we have taken an oath to not disclose the guest list. I can say that there are inventors, philosophers, and educators among the elite, along with some good, hardworking people.

I would hope that this annual event will continue on after our departure from this place. I wish that our children will carry on the tradition, though not all of us have children. Much knowledge and wisdom are shared on this weekend, believe it or not, conversations that, as a matter of fact, will change the course of our history. We have already enacted many changes in our ever-changing history of the Negro and as a result of these weekends.

A lot of people of wealth are present, though you would never know it by appearance, for we are all pretty much reserved. There are a few present who are perceived to be of one hundred percent European descent. This is one of the reasons for anonymity. Some of my guests have to arrive in the darkness of early morning and will depart the same way to maintain secrecy. We hold many well-kept secrets amongst our group. I said earlier that there were about ten guests, but that's only the ten that can be seen. In essence, there are about twenty guests. We have coined ourselves "The Privileged Group." We say that humbly because it is not in reference to financial means, but of the knowledge we possess of the past, the present, and the things to come. We are all part of the future. Some of our names will be known, while many of us will never be known to have had such an influence on the modern world.

Okay, back to the games. I was able to sneak away while our entertainer was entertaining. Oh, what a night, Mr. Man in the Moon. I love to see you come monthly; it reminds me of this holiday for some reason. I try and make it a point to look at you, Mr. Moon, when you return. It gives me such solace and that's about how often I get to take a break. I always take time out to relish in the beauty of the full moon. What a blessing. It signifies to me another thirty days lived.

Oh, my goodness, my rib sauce is smelling good! Oh, another part of the secret sauce is that I can tell when it's ready by removing the lid. If I remove the lid and take a deep breath through my nose and it causes me to cough, then I know it is ready. I have a mild, hot, and not-so-hot sauce as well as a sweet tasting one. I keep everyone's belly full so the head will not feel the pain in the morning from the grapes.

When my guests leave, they leave with pounds gained. This is one time when we can put away our airs of sophistication. If you do not burp, I am insulted. My guests leave with rejuvenated hope, knowledge, and wisdom, and I maintain the whist crown.

Until I see you again, Journal. My life you keep in your pages. What a wondrous life it is!

P.S. I am not dancing, but my sauces and you know who are!

CHAPTER 24
THE LAST NIGHT

D ear Journal,
I have to hire guards to ensure the security of my guests. We have to maintain a perimeter of sanctuary. Even though I have maintained that this is a holiday of respite, it is not. I emphasize to my guests that they are not to venture outside of our comfort zone because ladies of the night lay in wait for new victims to fall under their spell. Not to mention, those who would love to relinquish my guests of their purses. Regardless of wealth, no one is immune to the treacheries of others.

I advise my guests to place all of their worthy belongings in my safe. I have one of the finest safes manufactured by Wells Fargo. It is both waterproof and fireproof. There has to be rules to this holiday excursion, even though the neighborhood knows not to divulge or interrupt our goings on. There are always some who would like to test the waters, usually someone drifting into town. The rest know of my wrath. There have been a few occasions when we have had to literally bounce a few locals on their heads.

People from one extreme to the other, from religious to criminal minded, have tried to disrupt this very special holiday. From past experiences, outsiders, as you will, have learned to honor my privacy and that of my guests. There have been occasions when some of my guests have ventured out and tested the temptations that await them outside of my haven. Unfortunately, a few precious guests have been removed from my elite list. They understood once they were in a sober state. I did not exile them on their first violation. I give three strikes and then you are out. I love the game of baseball. These infiltrators and people of flight are few, but unfortunately, it does occur.

All but four have retired for the evening. These are my diehard whist players. We sometimes wager on the game. All proceeds go to a charity that will provide income to someone in need. We only bet for the sport of it, of course. Some say these are non-Christian activities, but churches use raffles and games of sport to raise funds. I am the founder of a church myself, but it seems that anything I am associated with is deemed to be that of the devil. I wonder how many of them I will see at the pearly gates when I go to the other side. It may sound like a great assumption that I will rest in the Kingdom of God, but I know the life that I live! All of those who claim to be righteous will not be saved. We start and end this holiday weekend with a prayer.

This weekend has all the theatrics of a play. As Shakespeare said, "We are all actors placed upon the stage of life. What role do you play?" I hear some type of domestic dispute going on nearby. I have sent my security to investigate. Many people booze it up on this holiday and tend to get violent. We hear a woman screaming for help. I will be right back, Journal. The dangers of the fermented grape …

CHAPTER 25
MEMORIAL DAY'S END

Dear Journal,
Morning has come, the final morning of this holiday. It has been an excursion for some, actually for all, even though some guests are local. It is an excursion in the sense that we are escaping from the normal routine in our individual lives. I have learned that, with my hectic life and schedule, an excursion can exist in the mind, never having to leave a room. A lot of times, while just standing in one spot, I have to remove my presence for an excursion. Okay, I'll call it a moment of prayer. At the same time, I can still hear a conversation and comment on it sensibly. It's an amazing gift I have. Being a host at my business, I have learned to carry on four or five conversations at a time.

My staff and I have prepared a feast for our departing guests. This time, I had actually just made the menu. The staff did all the preparation for this day. They were up with the roosters and the cows doing this. It is very hard for those trying to sleep through all the aromas floating through the air on this morning. The staff gets up early enough so those who want to attend church may do so.

They lay the spread out and I'll have others clean up. I usually let the cleaners take what is left over home and for the neighborhood.

They always try to surprise me with something new on the menu. They try to outdo themselves each time.

A few of the guests take a basket to go because their stomachs are not ready to digest anything, even water. I always tell them that to drink again what they had drank the night before. The snake that bit you will be the only antidote for the venom you had imbibed on this holiday. I also have some concoctions with lemonade or tomato juice and other ingredients to neutralize heavy heads or upset stomachs. I have a house punch that tastes like the nectar of the gods. I have found that the best neutralizer is just to eat a lot of fruit; apples and cantaloupe are the best. This is a failsafe remedy, in case someone does read this, Journal.

I serve my guests with the finest linen and purest silver utensils ever designed. My restaurant patrons have the best, but my guests have even better. Each year, I send the guests home with a utensil and a china plate engraved with my signature. Some of the guests have a whole set by now. I put a different flavored butter and honey into the basket. Life is good and Lexius Henson's food is good! It is phenomenal, and this is not just determined by me.

I order enough cigars to give a lucrative supply that should last if used sparingly. The guests try to stretch out their supply until the next visit, but that never happens. I usually have to ship some to them before we meet again. Sometimes, they will send a courier to guarantee the shipment. I know you are wondering whether I charge them. I do not, though you probably thought I did.

They literally beg for my recipes. I have had to threaten my friends for trying to lure my staff to their kitchens, but my staff is loyal and I treat them as family. I may show hard love to them, but they understand and appreciate all that I do for them and I appreciate all they do for me. They may not always feel that way, but as I've said, I show hard love. I believe it is a necessity when conducting this sort of business or any business, for that matter. Some people take kindness for weakness. Not all, but it only takes one bad apple to point out that weakness and you can be ruined in the blink of an eye.

Journal, as you know, I jump subjects regularly because I have so many thoughts on my mind and no one to talk to. This business I am in has also taught me the ability to readily change subjects. These are tumultuous times and so many are opinionated about our future. I have learned to be a good listener most importantly of all. Abraham Lincoln shared this mindset when he stated, "It is better to have remained silent and be thought of as a fool than to open up your mouth and remove all doubt." I have mastered that mindset, even though I have the answers to prove that I am not the fool and I have the answers to most people's lack of knowledge. I will let you make your own assessment; the next move is yours. I have strategically learned to nod my head and pose a question, which is the answer to other's lack of knowledge. There I go again, Journal, dancing with other thoughts. I am so glad you are the perfect dancing partner that can follow all of my steps.

Anyhow, all of my guests have departed and are on their merry way. They have enough to talk about until we meet again, God willing. All are glad they were in attendance. My goodness, this is my last day of the holiday, my retreat. I tire at the end of this event, but in the same token, I am rejuvenated with the vision and feeling that I have of hope and happiness and the reassurance that the human race will eventually unite and love one another and strive for the best for mankind. I have lost my train of thought; my oldest son has come to me.

CHAPTER 26
KIN FROM THE FUTURE

Dear Journal,

I must spend as much time as I can with my boys whenever possible. They have arrived early from visiting relatives in Savannah. They usually arrive the day after the holiday, but the family there had some things come up and they had to depart early. I am always glad to see them, of course, at any time.

I am getting up in age now. It's getting very hard to shake influenza these days. I use all types of concoctions to remain healthy. I eat a lot of garlic, drink aloe vera juices and olive oil, and boil all water that I drink, which I recommend to everyone. No one knows his time or his hour, and that is why I try to live right, so I will be ready to go home to my Father without regret or fear of damnation.

I hope that one day, Journal, my offspring will be able to read you, my confidant, my best friend. I know that the one from the future who comes to me in my dreams or conscience (I have not deciphered the difference yet), will be privy to my soul. I am trying to figure out what his purpose is.

There I go again, going into different subjects. It is like I am in a time warp, where I feel the presence of my kin from another time. It appears to be a time in the future because I see visions of things that I do not know of. It is as if he is reading every thought that I have shared with you, Journal, and he is questioning me on these matters for clarification. We are to a point of coexistence, as I have mentioned to you earlier, Journal.

Is he the other side of my conscience that I speak of, an alter ego, an entity of my being? Do I have the vision or power of insight into the future? I am perplexed at this point but I am not worried because he is a kindred spirit and I feel very comfortable when he is present. Am I going crazy? No, that I am not! I know that I am not because there are many who await the loss of my sanity. They wait for my demise to profit monetarily.

Just that quickly, I have gone back to the reality of my world. It is so peaceful, though, when he is present. I do not regret this life I have lived or my choices, but sometimes I wish there were three of me. In the same thought, it would just make matters thrice as complicated. My one life, I think, is enough for the lifetime of one hundred men. It is obvious, Journal, that I am tiring, but in my fatigue, I sometimes find some of the greatest thoughts. Until we meet again, Journal. Have a good morning!

CHAPTER 27
WEIL STOCKED

Dear Journal,
I have been smoking too many cigars lately. This usually occurs after my holiday.

I feel, once again, rejuvenated and ready to survive another year. Life is good and God is good to me! I have worked very hard to be where I am. I hope that my family, too, will have the same perseverance and characteristics and, if nothing else, knowledge and diligence. With that, they will prevail with richness, most importantly, internal richness of the soul and patience, which is a virtue, as it has been said. Finally, I hope that they always set goals that seem to be unattainable. The higher you set your goals, I believe the more attainable they become. Figure that one out. Never limit your dreams, no matter how far they appear to be out of reach.

Today is the day when my fishermen restock my supply. I also have them bring daily catches. The local fishermen mainly use the Savannah and Ogeechee Rivers for my catches of the day. The waters are plentiful because the Savannah River runs all the way to the ocean. They are liable to pull anything out of those waters. They bring perch, yellow perch, striper the size of small men, delectable trout, and large and small mouth bass. We have the sweetest tasting trout for reasons unbeknownst to me and so many types of pan fish. They bring me catfish the size of my torso, and I am not a small man. On occasion, mako shark will wander into the river, which is not good because they can devour a whole season of fish, but oh how I love to grill the mako shark. What a treat, with lemon, a dash of garlic, butter, and my special spices; it is one of my favorites.

We are not far from the ocean, where I am able to get fresh seawater fish and crustaceans. Don't get me started; I've already given up a recipe in my moment of jubilation. The portions I serve are so huge because I acquire the catch at such a good market price. Out of the Savannah we get sturgeon, which makes the finest domestic caviar. We have red drum, shad, and sunfish. We get gators as well. I have learned to cook the gator to make it so tender and palatable.

I have secret recipes for all of my swimming delights. Today is also the day when my hunters bring in their game. We get wild turkeys, a steady supply of venison, and snake. I have learned many ways, both new and old, to maintain my stock so it remains ever so fresh. Salt was the currency in days of yore, and I will share with you that salt is one of my ways of preserving meats and other things.

It has come to a point where my clientele dine at my restaurant for dinner every day instead of having dinner at home. The servants of these people appreciate it, but at the same time wonder if they will continue to be needed in the big house. They are sometimes assigned other tasks to justify the need of their labor. I mean no harm to these people, but this is what I do, and I do it well. This was also part of the reason for my expansion.

I have chosen a career where the Europeans do not care how much money I make at their expense. I have them under my spell. They are addicted like it is opium or alcohol. They are intoxicated by my culinary skills. There are many trades where the European has either bought the Negro out, destroyed them by force, or gone into partnership with them because of the profits they were earning. We ran a lot of mills, livery stables, and other businesses that required labor to maintain. Europeans could not lower themselves to perform these menial tasks, but they still ended up with ownership of these essential trades. I have had quite a few outside sources offer me these deals as well. Some offers were very lucrative, but they wanted me to run the business. I work for no other man, only God.

There have even been strong armed attempts to take over my business, but they didn't realize the muscle I possessed. Fires were set and my food suppliers were being delayed or accosted, or their goods were destroyed. That is the reason I had to learn to preserve my stock. I always have a plan B in place. It never got to plan C. Sometimes, you have to wait and "C," even though I have plans from A to Z.

One thing in my favor is that I am deeply rooted in my community, not only locally, but I have become world renowned. I have many backers. Locally and state wide, I have enforcers who ensure that my clientele's lifestyle and dinners are not interrupted. As they say, "A way to a man's heart is through his stomach." By no means will they have their dietary regimens interrupted. I have a militia of my own. I have made so much money, it is incredible.

CHAPTER 28
FLOODS

Dear Journal,
My enemy is not man these days. My enemy is a thing called Mother Nature. Her rainfalls have led to many an Augustan's demise. What a blessing that man is not my biggest fear, but God's providence, which is my natural fear. Praise the Lord, Hallelujah! In this day and age, the Negro wishes the floods would wash away the Europeans. As I have mentioned, Journal, I have purchased a five-story building. It still costs me when the levee does not hold, but not as much as other businesses. I am able to recoup much faster now, without much profit loss.

I literally have had people come to dinner in rowboats. They just could not pass up the opportunity to eat and entertain at my saloon. I get a big laugh out of this. My business neighbors have also learned to make the best of these annual Augusta floods. The cognac is unspoiled and the cigars are kept dry, but realistically, I have to consider other alternatives for revenue on a consistent basis.

I have purchased stock in a few sound ventures: steel, railroads, and banking. I have had the finest counsel on these investments.

Carnegie, Rockefeller, and Morgan all frequent my establishment when in this region. They make a point of it on their itinerary. One thing they request is that the other is not present. There is great animosity between the three richest men of the world. They live to outdo each other. It is not about the money, though that is a factor, but they are more concerned with who leaves the greatest legacy. That is what they tell me while under the influence. It is about power and control.

I have been fortunate to be of mulatto descent. Some have considered it a curse because mulattos are people with no certain identity. A few races were created from the victims of conquerors. A lot of this knowledge will never be shared in books to maintain the fallacy that there exists only a black and white race.

Even though these races have been given names, their blood-lines will never be disclosed. The Italians or Eastern Europeans were conquered by a great general by the name of Hannibal, even though "great" will never be associated with his name. This man marched an army of elephants through mountains to attain victory. He was victorious over a region that was made up of blue eyes and blond hair. After his conquest, breeding created a dark-haired, brown-eyed race, with features of the African. There are many regions of unpublished mulattos.

One can use these bloodlines in his favor or, at times, it can be used against him. When on the plantation, fairer skin allowed you to be enslaved in the Big House. To be known as a house Negro caused much dissention amongst those not living in Master's house. It allowed privileges that were not given to their dark-skinned kin.

Even when they are in town, the mulatto is allowed to look the European in the eye for a second. They are even allowed to have conversations, within limits of course. I have never had to experience these limitations, except a couple of times when in travel and my identity was questioned. After producing papers, I was able to look up, but still not stare. By the Freed Man Census, I have been classified as colored and on another as mulatto.

I have never been an enslaved man nor has anyone in my family, but I do understand and know the limitations of my color. By the time they mustered up the nerve to ask my lineage, I was deeply rooted into the community and their culture as an equal. I never tried to hide my background or my bloodline of European, Irish, British, Welsh, American Indian, and African descent. I was always ready to accept whatever perceptions they had of me.

What is ironic is that people of my own race were the ones who tested or questioned me. I am not ashamed of any part of me and people need to understand that. I am not trying to be one or the other, so why is it that you judge me? I am only being who I can be. I do not look down my nose at any of God's creations. When will we all learn this and take it to heart? We are all one. There needs to be unification of the human race. I know, Journal, it seems that I am riding the fence on race, but I am what I am—a man. Okay, Journal, I see that if I don't stop now, I never will. Once again, until we meet again …

I did not sleep well last night. I had dreams, visions, nightmares of things I don't understand. Anyhow, the show must go on, business as usual. There are threats of storms coming again, and I wonder if the levees will hold. We are a resilient community. We have rebuilt this town all too many times. Only the strong survive. It has become a social affair when we have a flood. To see aristocrats wading and playing in the high waters is such an amusement. Insurance companies are not enjoying this fiasco at all. Businesses are lost, people dead, dreams destroyed.

I have learned from these catastrophes. I have put money aside for "the rainy day." It is the truest saying here in Augusta, more so than any other place in these states. That saying had to be coined right here. As I have said many times, I invested in the old *Augusta Chronicle* building for many reasons, one being that it is a higher structure, where I would not be totally devastated by floods. I've had to replace one floor of the business, compared to a total business loss.

I have created dumb waiter systems to expeditiously move stock to higher floors. There were similar systems already implemented in the *Chronicle* building, but they were not designed to handle heavier equipment. Other merchants have observed my techniques and followed suit. Merchants reopen, but at a greater expense. I have conferred with city and government engineers to better learn how to develop our levees. We have improved upon our systems, but no one can control the flow of rain but God.

There have been days when I have considered throwing in the towel. I have been quite profitable and not frugal with my profits. The businesses that survive are the ones with the big investors behind them. The Goodyear company is here. We also have Rockefeller and Carnegie money invested here in Augusta. I am considered one of the wealthier ones also, but not at the level of the Rockefellers or Carnegies. I am well respected by the wealthy. I am often asked of my opinion on new business ventures. They heed to my advice. It has become a norm that my advice becomes a part of their dining experience. I wonder sometimes if it is because of my fine cuisine, my fine liquors, or my sound advice that they frequent my establishment. I do know they sought after my fine delicacies before I had given advice. They listen to me because I have great insight into the future. Every ounce that I have given has turned into pounds of worth. I, too, have profited from these conversations. They, too, share advice and opportunities that only few are privy to. I am invested in many profitable ventures due to networking.

I get first wind of new innovations and upcoming trends, like steel to make skyscrapers, as they are being called, and trains to transport the steel, cattle, and produce, amongst other commodities that are in great demand. I also import and export. The states have a large demand for the fine china, furniture, etc. of their Irish, British, and Welsh backgrounds. I have my own line of fine china that I have personally signed, along with silverware to complement my exquisite table settings and my building. I have oriental rugs, tapestry from India, and other fine artwork. I begin to tire, Journal, rest well. Until we meet again.

CHAPTER 29
BARTENDER

Dear Journal,
I have a bartender like no other. He entertains my guests with a one-man show of bartending skills. He can throw a shot of liquor from one glass to another at arm's length without spilling a drop! He can flip a bottle into midair while opening and pouring a drink at the same time. I am not exaggerating, Journal. He tosses the bottle around his back and under his legs. It is truly a culinary exhibition. He has drinks that he can set afire and you can drink from them while lit without burning a whisker. He can slide a beer mug, make it spin down the long bar, and the handle would be turned to your grip when it stopped every time, without spilling a drop.

I tell him that he is one of the greatest philosophers of our time. He has stories on top of stories, never ending, time after time. The Greeks entertain with the same skills, I have read. He never forgets what a man drinks, even if he had only served you once. The patrons reward him handsomely. He is as frugal as I am about waste. He shares his rewards with the waiters and the other staff. I ask for none of his profits. They say that I am one of the richest Negros in the South, but I beg to differ. After observing his gratuities, I wonder if I went into the right trade.

He creates a lot of revenue for me. He has clientele that come in just for his sideshow. I retract that; he is on the main stage and he is the top act. I make great profits on his liquor sales. He also pushes the sale of my cigars, oysters, and other appetizers that I have available. He can slice open eight oysters at a time with one swipe of his sharp blade. I tried it once and almost cut my arm off. He carves fruit and other food with the skills of the finest sculptor. He could make a full bust out of an olive or a cherry. He makes most of the garnishes for my entrees, and oh what he can do with a block of ice! Not only that, but he is an artist that makes caricatures of the patrons. I do not know what I would do without him. He has an apprentice, but I do not believe he will be able to pass on all of his unique skills to him.

I sure would hate to be the man that ever makes him mad after seeing his skills with a knife. There is one story about a man who had pulled a gun, and my bartender cut the man's fingers so quickly that when the man went to pull the hammer back, his fingers fell off and the gun fell to the floor. The man picked up his fingers and ran. What he planned to do with the fingers, I do not know. One finger was found still on the trigger, in position to pull. He did not come back for the pistol. As a matter of fact, he left town.

My bartender was hired out to make centerpieces for gala affairs; that was my idea. At first, this feature was exclusive for my restaurant, but I always shared entrepreneurial opportunities with those around me, my people. I put money into my community and I showed those who would listen how to make money and capitalize on the individual skills they possessed, no matter how insignificant they might have thought they were.

Everything I see, just about, I figure out how I can make it profitable. Some may hate me, but some love me indiscreetly because they know what I do to better ourselves. I teach and preach unity. I am only different in skin color and my parental heritage. I cannot help the fact that I am a mulatto, that my family and I have always been free and educated, and my father was a doctor. I turn up my nose to no man. I just don't tolerate a lot of nonsense. I will even tolerate ignorance, for many have no control over that; however, I do think there is a difference between ignorance and common sense. Lack of common sense results in nonsense.

Back to my staff. They are quite a menagerie of personalities. It is not just myself who has made my business successful. Each one has proven to be loyal and an intricate part of my rise to becoming one of the top restaurateurs of this day. My reviews have been the finest a restaurant can receive. These reviews come from all parts of the globe, from patrons who have visited while in Augusta. I have achieved a great name for myself and a legacy, but I am afraid that it will not be passed on. My children show no interest in continuing my business. I have dedicated my entire adult life to this business. It saddens me to know that it will probably not be passed on to my family. I will eventually have to sell.

My only hope is in my dreams, my nightly visions of the one that comes to me in my private times and thoughts. I don't know if he even really exists or will exist, but he appears to be so real. He has a fervor and great interest in my skills. It gives me some type of hope that Lexius Henson will live on, a legacy.

Have I created a hope in my subconscious to continue my fervor for existence or is it an epiphany of my legacy? I pray so. When my body leaves this place, this physical existence, I pray that my spirit self will allow me to see if this person of family will really exist and carry on my torch for the unification of the human race and, secondly, my recipes.

Anyway, it gives me strength and hope that is not given to me by anyone else except Sarah, my second wife. My children reap my benefits, but I do not see an extension of myself in their personas. My family has begun to spread out to other states and I have heard that they are not taking their identity with them. This saddens me, of course, but I will not grieve or mourn prematurely.

I will remain positive, as I always have been, but in the same token, realistic.

Journal, I am wound up now with so much to say. My physical shell tires and I must rest. My mind never sleeps. Until we meet again, Journal. Good morning.

CHAPTER 30
CLEANSING OF SOULS

Dear Journal,

I not only run a business, restaurant, and a place of goods, I secretly run what one would call a seminar. It is a seminar of self-worth. I have also taught my community hygiene. I have published a pamphlet that I have discreetly distributed. We have many that do not know of hygiene, such as brushing your teeth and washing your body, specifically, your private parts and armpits. I especially stress combing hair to fit this society, as many have slept on bare dirt floors. I teach them to keep their abode free of critters, mites, and fleas, as insects carry disease. I have shown them how to use caustic solutions to sanitize their places of rest. I teach them to boil their utensils, linen (which few have), and clothing. They are already classified as unclean souls, spiritually and physically. I have explained thoroughly the importance of these practices.

I readily supply a safe soap that will not cause harm to their skin. I tell them that their clothes may be ragged, but keep what little you have clean, without odor, and buttoned into place. If you only have one button, place it in the center. I supply buttons as well.

With freedom upon us these days, we need to raise our awareness of the European ways. Many rumors are being spread to the northerners that we carry disease and other undesirable attributes that can or could disrupt the European's household. They try to suggest that we carry sexual diseases as well. These are all used as deterrents as they plant seeds to persuade others not to take the Negro in. They do this to label our whole society. They want the Negro to remain in the South.

One thing that has been allowed more in these days is church, religion, and spiritualism. They believe the Negro to be heathens, so they have allowed us to be made aware of the Bible and its teachings, even though it is still illegal in most parts for us to learn and read. There are also missionaries present. They allow it because they believe it to be a calming of the Negro spirit. They do not know that this allowance of religion was the beginning of true freedom. It not only gave us hope, but education at the same time.

Not much was given to the Negro, but religion was readily preached. They thought we were the devil himself, even though lynching and moral injustices were being practiced as a norm and continue as I speak. Religion taught us to have faith, hope in something, in God. It was still hard for many to grasp religion when the Bible taught about a God of love and fairness, while the Negro was still being persecuted.

What gave and still gives strength were the stories of David and Goliath, Daniel in the lion's den, Job's trials and tribulations, and Moses's exodus from slavery, which they told us had a different meaning when asked what it meant. These are the stories that the Negro directly related to their existence and plight. As we know, Job overcame, Moses freed his people, Daniel slew the lions, and David brought down the giant, Goliath.

Religion is a bandage placed on our wounds of slavery. Their practice of religion appears to be superficial. The Negro thanks the European for religion.

My kin from another time tells me that great religious leaders will change time as we know it. He tells me they will be persecuted and executed as well. He tells me of things that are hard to conceive, but I can tell by his dress, vocabulary, and demeanor that change has occurred over the years.

You had your portion of people who thought religion was a hoax. They could not understand why a loving God would let his children suffer so much. Eventually, they come to understand that they were included in the Bible as they cried out, "Thank you, Father!" They felt great anguish in witnessing the atrocities but also felt the presence of a higher being touch their souls.

I had to start my own church, as I have stated to you earlier, Journal. They called me a godless man because I served alcohol and tobacco at my establishment and allowed non-Christian, adulterous, and lascivious acts to occur because of the services I render, perpetuating sin of the highest level. This is far from the truth. I do not run a brothel. I do not allow such acts to occur in my parlors. If these things happen, it is without my sanctioning. There are far more adulterous acts occurring outside of my place than inside my place, and that is still not saying that they occur. If you ask me, Journal, I must tell you no lie. I have heard of these goings on, but I cannot close my business based on rumors. I do not, and I repeat, do not allow or sanction these ungodly acts. I am a Christian man.

Jesus drank wine that they say was not fermented, but that can't fully be true. I make a delectable dandelion wine myself and know the ingredients and process of making wine. All wine was not served as soon as the grapes were crushed. The same methods used then are the same methods of production being used now. The Catholics use wine in their communion ceremony. I am not making a mockery of Jesus, saying that he was a drunkard, nor were his apostles. Well, a few were before their conversion. The Bible states that not the bishop shall partake of the grapes. It also says that as long as you use the grape, not to induce drunkenness.

No one will disallow me to worship. We have separatism, even in religion. What is worse is the different shades of our race. The mulattos and the darker skinned Negros do not worship at the same place. The Europeans have taught us to discriminate amongst our own race. Nothing is sacred. Once again, conquer and divide. My church is the first organized church of its kind in America.

The war is over, but there is an even greater war occurring today, greater than we have ever seen, because it was not designed to be seen. I truly believe this war will be cloaked for many years to come.

I have personally heard the strategies of their battle plan. I find no flaws in it, unless people of my sort or the authors of this strategy have a change of heart and discontinue the implementation of this plan. I, too, am a victim of this plan. Journal, you will often hear me refer to the Negro, or sometimes the community, or my people. I, too, have been guilty of this discrimination, most of the time unknowingly. That is how it is designed to be. You don't even know that you are being your own worst enemy. In using these different name tags, I inadvertently discriminate.

I am a wise man, aware of the strategy, but I readily succumb to the warfare. Those who follow my death, wake up and be aware of all that you say and do. I reiterate the strength of this planned warfare. I have philosophized and strategized many things, but none to the depth of this holocaustic design. How can this seed be uprooted before it germinates? It has already been planted.

Constant enlightenment and awareness is the means to start rectifying this problem of disparity. It is necessary to always seek knowledge from both sides to unravel this riddle, not to dwell upon transgression. Just being aware that the plan exists is a start in the right direction towards discovery. Move forward, without hate and malice, seeking the solution of being one race, the human race.

I started off talking about hygiene and got into cleansing of the souls. I have taught my community to be honest and true to their handshake; it is all we have. I have found that European's do believe that the Negroes honor this tradition as well. This is one attribute that the Europeans honor in their culture, and now we have been allowed to follow the custom.

I perform a daily inspection of my staff for hygiene and neatness. I line them up like soldiers in my war of perfection. There should be no dirt under the nails and no odors, even when they're not in the presence of our customers. Our customers like to come in and readily commend our staff. I teach them to have pride in their work. This is a reflection of me, their families, and themselves. The locals know who is in the kitchen. It trickles down to their families for favor in the community. They are all uniformed in the finest linen wares. I handle the expenses. No other place does this in the South. Only some establishments in the North and abroad maintain this level of professionalism. I was raised in this manner due to my father being a physician and our family having hired help of different races. They were treated like family as well, mind you, not slaves.

I could have very easily followed my father into his profession. I chose, instead, to be a "healer of appetites." My father did not hold this against me, for he knew he had planted the proper seeds to produce a healthy plant of sustenance, a flower with a fragrance to be remembered, a plant that is deeply rooted.

My father was of great influence in my life. He believed in being educated to the highest level of education available. He also believed in an individual highlighting one's self-worth and ideology. He believed in finding what was best suited for you. Most families promote that you follow in their footsteps. If you were a blacksmith, then so was your son.

My father was a dreamer, philosopher, and an inventor, as I am. I guess that is why I will not hinder or judge the careers of my offspring. I will not deny the fact that I wish they would continue my legacy, as my father wished of me. I want my business to pass on for many generations, without end. My kin who comes to me in my dreams expresses that he continues my skills, but not yet to the level of my accomplishments.

My father financed Charles's and my dreams. It is so important, I believe, that you allow your children to explore who they are. However, you need to lay down a firm foundation on what it is you do and lead by example. Allow them options for opportunities, for desires in their hearts, within reason.

Short of the degree required, I could be a doctor. My father taught me that life is

without limitations. Though you may be shackled, no one can take your thoughts and no matter what you are going through, no matter the storm, no one can peel back your scalp and steal your dreams. With hope, your mind will always be free; you can shackle my body, but not my mind or soul. Even if your dreams never materialize physically, they are your sole property. You have the ownership of self. My father taught us to find an Eden within ourselves. Peace lies within. No one possesses a key or password to your soul to enter without permission. We are all supernatural beings. We are the children of a supernatural creation. The only limitation is your imagination.

I come from South Carolina, where most share the same mindset and outlook on the creation of mankind and its existence. Granted, the world is changing and restrictions have been placed upon certain men and cultures, but the mindset should always be to persevere, utilize thought, and continue to grow in the mind. Find peace within, regardless of the pain and the rain.

We are a resilient people. Never forget that all the world isn't your enemy. Don't be bitter. The enemy truly lies within. We create the walls of ignorance if we manifest hate. Pray for your enemies, as hard as it may be. Pray that they may have a change of heart. If nothing else, it will give you an inner peace that no man can steal.

Despite what is portrayed, we have no true hate against our aggressors. Once again, we don't have the luxury of the time it takes to hate. It takes a lot of energy and time to manifest such an emotion. Two of the most powerful emotions are love and hate. It takes more muscles to frown than it does to smile. Hate is spread to perpetuate war between races and cultures. This is necessary to keep those on the fence of prejudice. If we all knew the truth, we would jump to the side of righteousness, but they try and keep us mesmerized by their idealism. The Negro does not hate the European.

Part of the plan is to isolate heritages to make us feel like a lesser breed. We live day to day and hour to hour, sometimes minute to minute. Who has time to hate? We only have time to survive. Some have limited choices because of their economic situations, but it should never be used as a tool for their demise, as it has been devised. Thinking of another day is a luxury to many. My kin from another time tells me that this still exists in his day. He says that it is even more prevalent. He tells me that many children believe they have grown old if they reach the age of twenty-one. That is sad, very sad. That tells me that the plans I have overheard were as strong as I suspected them to be.

Facing diversities in this age is just a reflex, like breathing. It is natural during these times, though it saddens my heart that it is so. I have read that the great conqueror Hannibal cried himself to death because he knew he could not rid the world of people who shared his mindset of domination of one's soul.

A false war has been created as manipulation for the elites to stay in control. I consider myself a learned historian and I have observed that this has been a tactic from the onset of civilization. When does this stop? How do we stop it? Can we stop it? Yes, I believe we can. I pray that this journal is passed on with my wisdom and insight on how we can. My kin from another time weeps, just as I do on this subject but he, too, believes there is hope.

He reveals to me that there have been great changes among the races. Some have been superficial to quiet the natives. He also tells me that changes in stone have been made as well. He uses the term "Keep hope alive," Journal. He tells me that a great man of his time uses this phrase on his platform for peace. He laughs as he tells me that it is related to John Hope. He tells me that this person is from the same school as John Hope, which I do not understand. He tells me that he cannot share the future of John Hope, for I would understand.

The irony of all of this is that the Negro is not enslaved only by the Europeans. They have enslaved their own race. They are under the power and rein of the elite that rule. We are all being fired upon with the same weapon. We must find common ground in order for us to survive. I refer to "us," not as Negro, European, Asian, or Indian, but as the human race. We are the majority, but we are not in rule. Once again, Journal, all pawns in their kingdom are expendable as soldiers for their cause.

We must awaken to a new train of thought. Their arrogance toward their own is as great as it is to the Negro. They despise and abhor the have nots and the Negro almost equally. We are being subjugated by imperial rule.

This reminds me of a joke, if I will, Journal. Three men went to hell together, one European, one African, one Asian. The devil was giving them a tour through Hades. He showed them a room with three doors, where people who were on fire were shoveling coal for all eternity. The devil told them that at the end of this tour, the men would have to make a choice of which room they'd share their eternity together. So they proceeded to the other room, where the tortured souls shoveled manure into another room. The men were all thinking, *This is not for us.* So they went into the next room, where manure was also being shoveled, and there stood souls sipping tea, standing up to their knees in manure. They all huddled together and thought maybe this was the best of their choices. Standing in warm manure that wasn't on fire, sipping tea for all eternity didn't seem so bad. So they agreed that this was the room they would all choose. The devil handed them their tea and as he was leaving the room, a great bell sounded off and the men wondered what it meant. Before the devil shut the door for all eternity, he turned around and said, "Okay, tea break is over. Everybody, back on their heads."

The moral of the story is we are all up to our necks in manure. What appears to be is not always as it seems. There should have been questions asked. Race does not make a difference when we are placed in the same space.

I'm still laughing, Journal. Did you get the joke? I did!

CHAPTER 31
POLYGENISM

Dear Journal,
I am engulfed into a book about polygenism, a term that has a definition that is only privileged to a few. One of my patrons left it behind. I am certain, now, that they leave these materials behind to give me enlightenment on what the powerful minds are planning. Polygenism is the study of race, racism, and species, and the characteristics of the human race and species. This study justified conquering people of a lesser race, or, I should say, slaughtering a race for the betterment of the Europeans' way of life. This was necessary because they were supposed to be Christians and it would go against the Sixth Commandment that states, "Thou shall not kill," and the Bible's teaching to "love thy neighbor as thy self." So not only did they alter their religious beliefs with polygenism, but they justified their future rule to perpetuate the same.

These are studies from some of the supposed greatest minds and philosophers of all times. It is not actually a book, but a loose-leaf folder of the study. I have researched libraries to see if there had been something published on this matter. It appears this is the first study of its kind. I have been privileged to receive access to a lot of first-hand knowledge. It seems that after much indulgence of whiskies and cognacs, the urgency of my patrons' meetings in my place leaves their minds for a moment of relaxation.

I secure much knowledge from the absence of sobriety. I always return the material that I read. They don't have a clue the next morning as to the whereabouts of their works. I never let on that I have thoroughly scanned and imbibed the secret books of knowledge and enlightenment. Sometimes, Journal, I believe they leave them behind to test my allegiance and loyalty.

We have a diversity of guests. The gentleman that left the study behind was of German descent. Also present were some French gentlemen and a couple of men with dialects I could not decipher by their accents. They were having some type of convention, a convention that was not publicized. Our guests are also diversified in their thoughts on slavery, some for and some against.

I have found subjects on polygenism in other books, but they had not coined a name for it. It is incredible to me the time that some races have spent conquering races of lesser resources. Journal, as I have previously told you, I am aware that there are about five families that rule this planet. That is, they rule all European countries, those of Africa, and North America. It appears to me that the Asians still have their own rule but they, too, have been conquered in some regions. The Commission, as I call them, are pretty much in total reign of power. It seems that it goes beyond attaining wealth. It appears to be about power in maintaining their ways of living and their mindsets. I have overheard them stating that they have all the riches in the world that they want. It then becomes a competition of who has the most power. Meanwhile, they are playing chess with our lives and our souls. We are just pawns being played, sacrificed to attain their victories. Our souls mean absolutely nothing to them.

I believe these people are devising ways to disrupt the close relationships that whites have with Negroes in this day, so they do not forget that the white person is superior to the Negro. Contrary to belief, mass hatred against the Negro does not exist. White people sometimes put on a cloak of deceit, portraying hatred for the Negro in the presence of their peers. They are forced to be this way.

I recall the conversations of endearment about their slaves. They considered them as family and treated many as such. I would like to believe that this was a norm here in Augusta, but outside agitators perpetuate racism. It is necessary to portray hate because of this polygenism study. I wonder how many slave owners were placed in the same predicament of hate. I have overheard from some of the stringent slavery promoters that this is necessary to continue rule. I believe that if a group of those who are pro-slavery and wealthy would stand up against this, then things would change, but no one wants to be the sacrificial lamb.

The one who comes to me in my dreams tells me that in the future, there will be whites who do just that. He also tells me that they, too, will be prosecuted, persecuted, and even assassinated as Lincoln was. The European laughs at the fact that they have so much control over what is becoming the majority, the Negro. I know why putting things on paper is so powerful. We are living in times when a document is taken as truth. This so-called Declaration of Independence was supposed to be a guideline for our country, but we live so far from the truths of the elaborate document. It says that all men are heard equally. I didn't read anywhere in this declaration where it stated that people of color were to be alienated.

That is why these new studies are being documented and entered into law without a vote. The scholars of polygenism are nothing more than men of influence. The majority of them are just regular physicians. They are creating names for their personal agendas to justify their means. People actually give grants to these people to make studies. The one who comes to me in my dreams tells me that I cannot imagine how they sophisticatedly mask our Constitution and laws. The things that I share with him about my time saddens him so. He tells me that I, too, would be saddened if I could observe that much has not changed from my day. He tells me that the same wolf is in control, only with a different type of attire to disguise.

Whites discriminate when hiring by saying the Negro person is not qualified for the job. They say they do not possess the skills needed. They use educational degrees as a basis as to whether the person has the skills to perform the job. He tells me that the Negro is still limited in resources for higher education. This was one of the ways I'd overheard how they would limit the advancement of the Negro. The one in my dreams from another time tells me that there were laws that make employers hire a quota of minorities as tokens only. He also tells me that these laws were rescinded later on.

This tells me that by the implementation of polygenism, the seeds were planted. These seeds became full grown plants, nourished by the mindset that was instilled into generations to come. I knew that when I read the study, this would play a major role in the non-unification of the human race and, instead, promote separatism.

The one in my dreams also tells me that, on the lighter side of things, some companies do not care what color you are, as long as you make them money. He also tells me that there are more black millionaires than I could possibly imagine. In the same breath, he tells me that these new-money millionaires do not come back to bring prosperity to their communities. He tells me that some are kept engrossed by what they do, while the European keeps them running in circles to maintain their riches.

This somewhat reminds me of my situation. They are not intimidated by my riches,

but they do not readily take to me empowering others. That is why I secretly endow many people in my community. He tells me that interracial marriages occur more than I would imagine, though; however, when some of the rich Negros are placed in the European environment, they are alienated from marrying within their own race to prevent sharing their wealth within their communities. He says that most of these wealthy marriages end up with the black man losing everything and the European wife retaining all the wealth. This was not part of my dream of the unification of races. He tells me that sometimes the thrill of eating the forbidden fruit causes the black man to partake in what he considers a delicacy. He is for unification of all races as I am, but he believes the motivation for all races should be love.

As I have stated earlier to you, Journal, I believe we are all of the same first seed. The Negro of my time loved his Nubian princess and abhorred the use of his body by his master's mistress. The Negro is blackmailed into having relations with the European woman by the threat that she will cry out molestation, which means death. My kin from another time tells me that once the Negro of wealth attains riches, he is discouraged from being around his own race for threat of loss of endorsements. I don't understand all of this because he does not give me the total concept of what perpetuates these occurrences. He is limited in what he can share with me in fear that it may alter the future, but I do get the gist of it.

———————

To be blind to all the accomplishments of Negroes is to be absent in one's mind. It has taken all the knowledge of the world's people to bring it where it is today. No one race can take full credit for a monopoly on inventions and wisdom. We all take something from another culture. That is why I believe God made so many diverse people.

A few people with PhDs attached to their names have been allowed to dictate doctrine on race. They quickly grabbed ahold of these views, only because it was profitable in most cases. Then after a while, they really come to believe these philosophies because these doctrines have been injected into their blood streams over a period of time. You want to talk about evolution; this was a man-made evolution.

Some share infinite wisdom, while many share infinite ignorance. It scares me because these are the people who are going to determine our future for centuries to come. I believe this wholeheartedly and I am of unbiased opinion. I am both races, to which I share the love proportionally. I believe in equality. Judge a man by his character, by what he produces, and by his word.

I have met as many shiftless Europeans as I have met Negros; yet, I do not hate either. We must be made aware of the fact that racism has no race. Whites of lesser financial means are treated as badly as the Negro, but they will still call a Negro a nigger. They still believe they are better, by race association and heritage, than the Negro.

The poor, desolate European man is not publicized. Many live in worse conditions than the Negro on the same lands. Why is this not spoken about? They are treated as poorly by their employers, yet they have no unity with their Negro brothers and sisters who share the same plight. It is amazing to see how they keep us blinded from the truth. We are all the same.

I, for one, am not blinded by the light of racism. I share the truth with those who will listen and won't go behind my back with these lessons. Many throw daggers as soon as you turn your back and will go and alert those people who do not want me sharing enlightenment. I have to be very careful because I could lose my livelihood and my life. I have seen many hanging from a tree, including a man who had been disemboweled. I have seen all of the atrocities that a man could possibly do to another human being. I have seen the same done to women and children as well. Memories that can never be erased. Things that no person should ever witness.

Some of my patrons have come to me with warnings regarding the ill behavior of some Negroes, which I have expeditiously conveyed to the targeted person or group. Some heeded the advice and others didn't. Some had to pack up and leave with only the shirts on their backs because, as it was conveyed to me, "the law was broken." Even though there are many strange and unfair laws, there are some unwritten laws that are specifically for the Negro. For example: no selling or vending after sundown, no looking a white person in the eye, always addressing white people as sir or ma'am, and absolutely no touching white people, mistakenly or not. All of these things I am allowed to do. I, being a rational minded man, could see why my people of color dislike and sometimes hate me. I have never walked with a badge of arrogance or superiority on my lapel. I am not angry at the other side of my heritage.

A large number of foreign investors have a major stake in the progress of our land. Many of them have yet to set foot on this land, yet they dictate policy on how this country is run. Those who have touched our land have dined at my place. I have the secrets of the world under my roof, the ruling powers of our day. I dare not mention these people of high importance to you, Journal. It could cost both my life and yours. Kings and queens, princes and princesses, generals, governors, mayors, presidents and cabinet members, founders of steel corporations and railroads, and banks have graced my place with unannounced arrivals. Many make it a point to return to my place.

Many laws were passed in my presence, without a vote ever being tallied. Ways of life have been established. I, too, set ways of life in etiquette and dining. I use finger blows and oshibori towels as royalty does before and after dining. They sample the wines and cognacs before ordering. Not many places offer this royal treatment in the South. There are some places that have heard of my service and are trying to duplicate it.

I have set standards on what the wealthy expect in a dining experience. Here I go again, jumping on my own bandwagon, but, Journal, you are the only one I am able to jump on with. I want to expound further on polygenism, racism, and origin later; this is a note, Journal. Remind me. Boy, do I jump subjects. I always end up talking about my restaurant. I guess other than enlightenment, that is all I think about.

Until we meet again, Journal. I bid you good morning.

CHAPTER 32
THE SUNDAY LIQUOR LAW

Dear Journal,

I was fined and summoned to court for serving alcohol on Sunday; yet, I was told by the mayor that this was allowed. It appears that an undercover agent of the court was sent to my establishment on a couple of occasions to see if I had been abusing the law by serving alcohol on Sunday. The agent of the court stated that this was my regular practice.

Mind you, this was a person who ran up a large tab and had been inebriated and obnoxious on occasion. He'd had to be gentlemanly removed as well. He was not of social means but used his position to live life like a barrister. He had no title or affiliation with the courts legally but was of relation to the mayor.

I have boarders to whom this law does not apply. If they choose to sip on Sunday, then that is their business; they reside here. Times are changing, and the community is being influenced by outsiders.

I hear many plans from the controllers of our community as well as outsiders. They are trying to limit non-white business owners. They are not really plans, but a map. They don't have to make plans;

NO TIME TO HATE

they just enforce these things upon us. They have it all laid out, and it will have an effect for hundreds of years. I share this information with a very limited view on these matters. I cannot sit by and not utilize this information for the equality of men. Not that sharing this information can immediately change anything, but it will at least arm us with their strategies. In any type of war, one needs to know the strategy of the adversary.

My community thinks I am part of the conspiracy as well. They are blinded by my heritage and skin color. We have the same issues, whether they know it or not. I place free thought into their minds while trying to prevent another Civil War. I make the important civil rights leaders of our time totally aware of their mindset.

I teach them to be aware, pay close attention, and play their roles accordingly, because our time will come. Maybe this will not happen in our time, but it will be a cornerstone for generations to come. I have been loaded with ammunition, the knowledge of things to come.

There I go again, drifting. Back to the case. My attorney, Mr. Webb, put one of my boarders on the stand to testify that he'd heard the mayor state that I could serve alcohol to my regular boarders on Sunday. The mayor was then asked to take the stand and asked how the accusation that I had broken the law was given to the courts. The mayor refused to answer. He was then asked to identify the informant. He refused to answer again. Then Mr. Christian, the chief of police, was placed on the stand. He was asked to reveal the same, and he refused to disclose the person as well. He said the case was reported to the mayor and not to him. Lieutenant King reported the same.

I would never have taken the liberties upon myself to ignore the law. My attorney stated in his argument that there could be no crime without a union of act and intention, and it was clear that I, the defendant, did not intend to violate the law and ought to be acquitted. The mayor said it was evident that I'd misunderstood what he'd said, and I did not intend to violate the law, and the judge summarily dismissed the case. Now, mind you, the mayor has partaken of the grape in my establishment on a Sunday, but never inside my saloon. I have separate quarters reserved for boarders, where the alcohol was served.

156

It appears I am always litigating something. I guess I am blessed to have the knowledge and opportunity to do so. I find it challenging and I somewhat enjoy it. As I told you earlier, Journal, law would be my second choice of career. My kin from another time tells me that he, too, loves the law and has been tested many times, only to prevail.

This was pretty much an open and close case so as not to cause embarrassment to the mayor and his staff. The issue was derived from an outside agitator, who is continually trying to disrupt my livelihood. There is no doubt that many have it in for me from both races. This is why I make sure I know the laws and abide by them. I know I am not beyond reproach, as many would like to think.

This was just another day in the life of Lexius Henson. I have become accustomed to this. All it does is strengthen me. It just increases my cellar of knowledge. My stock is vast and increases. When will they learn? My kin from another time laughs because he lives through the same repeated scenarios, like a mirror of my life. Maybe that is why he has come to me in my thoughts and dreams.

Now, on the other side of the coin, I am finding out that in my situation and others, race has nothing to do with all of this. It is all about economic survival and control. I am finding that if you can find a spot in the white man's structure that does not disrupt their flow, you are allowed a little piece of the pie. I don't even need a whole slice. I am satisfied with the crumbs, which allow me to live a very lucrative life. The problem is that my business creates more than one helping of the pie, and there lies the threat.

If the world would learn that everyone does not require a whole slice and is satisfied with what they are allotted, we would be okay. But the greedy want total control of the portions being served. That is their obsession, greed and control. They want us to make the pie for them; yet, they don't want to pay a fair wage for our labor. Then they want to take the pie and run. Do they not understand that we've put the ingredients in the pie and baked it? We must not sell all of our recipes in life! Sometimes, we have no choice, but many times, we go for quick profit without having the vision for long-term benefits. The European takes full advantage of our lack of knowledge. I share this mindset with many of my fellow non-white businessmen.

There are enough resources on this earth to maintain all of us. That is how I believe God designed it. Does He not take care of the sparrow as well? There are some wise men in our times who have the knowledge but are limited in resources, unable to fully develop their inventions; that is where the European comes into play. We need to form a coalition and protect our own knowledge. We are isolated in different regions and not able to put our knowledge and resources together.

My kin from another time tells me that we will eventually network to put organizations of color together. He also tells me that they are more superficial than anything else. He says it is a step in the right direction, but it is only on paper and they still lack the proper monetary investments that are necessary. He tells me that everyone is still afraid of investing in their own race, in fear of losing what they have acquired.

My kin from another time tells me that they use the same tactics that were used in my lawsuit to thwart advancement. He tells me that we eventually fall under the pressure or sell. He tells me that the black-owned businesses with black agendas are bought by Europeans, who then sell with their own agendas, from media to clothing. Is there such a word as equality? Not in this lifetime.

Even though I am free, and my family has been free for as far back as I can trace my lineage, there will always be restraints. Life has been a culmination of restraints ever since the devil was cast upon this earth. The devil is what I call our weaknesses. I should call it the devil's strength. For those who don't believe in the devil, I will call it "destiny that is placed upon you by another man." There are two sets of rules in the world: God's rule and the devil's, or man's, rule. Once you stop following God's rules, the devil comes in to dictate. Part of the devil's rules are greed, adultery, envy, and deception.

We forget that God's rule supersedes that of the devil and should be the only rule that we follow. We know that but, still, we acknowledge the rules of man first before we apply the rules of God, thereby subjecting ourselves to the devil's deception. Adhere to the Word first, and God will show you the route to journey upon, and you will beat the deceptions of life. I will relate this to business as well. Clear your mind first and find out whether this venture is sanctioned by God and not by the immediate allure of profit.

What are the causes and effects in my life if I choose to partake in a venture? Never look at the immediate reward because that is the devil's ploy. As the saying goes, "All that glitters is not gold." Always know there are options; don't panic!

CHAPTER 33
SARAH BEALE

Dear Journal,

Sarah Beale, my wife, but not the wife who bore my children, was accosted today in our upstairs living quarters. She said it was Charles, a man who used to work for me. Sarah was sitting at the table, and in walked this man. She said he spoke nothing to her and beat her as if she were a man, like a master would beat one of his runaway slaves.

Sarah appears to be of delicate stature, but she proved otherwise in her ability to withstand the punishment. Sarah was quite bruised and cut from blows and she was left in much pain. Her body was in physical and mental shock.

This occurred while I was downstairs, working in the restaurant. He knew our schedule well and took full advantage of the situation. The attack was of precise timing. He appeared to be as rabid as a dog, without foaming of the mouth. Sarah stated that he did not appear to be inebriated, nor could she smell any alcohol. She said that he had the stare of a crazed maniac. Sarah said she didn't even have a second to ask him what he wanted. The maid was in the rear of the house, tending to her duties as she usually does at that time of day. It is very hard to hear from one end of the house to the other.

Sarah's injuries were mainly to her head, stomach, and back. He had blackened her eye closed. I still cannot believe she didn't suffer any broken bones or a concussion. An even worse thought is that she could have been killed.

Sarah did not even have time to scream, just time to survive. She said it seemed like she'd endured this brutal, sadistic punishment for an eternity; but we later discovered, after putting the time line together with the maid, that Charles was only in there for a couple of minutes. The maid had just left Sarah and went to the rear of the house. This makes me wonder if there was a conspiracy between the maid and Charles. The maid has been with me for some time now. She was here before I'd wed Sarah. I cannot take anything for granted now. There are many theories going through my mind, too many to rationalize at this time.

My first concern is that of Sarah's physical and mental wellbeing. The authorities are in search of Charles as we speak, Journal. I have put my own resources on the streets as well. As suddenly as he'd appeared, he disappeared. He had not been around much about a week or two prior to the attack.

Charles did not really have that much family in this area. He had a couple of cousins and an aunt. I am somewhat accustomed to altercations geared toward me, but never ever toward my family. Sarah is a quiet, reserved individual with a kind heart and she does not venture far from the nest. It was meant as revenge against me.

Only a spineless man would attack another man's family. It is good that he escaped before he was in my presence. I am a very fair and forgiving man, but there are limits. Charles crossed all lines of forgiveness. There could have been only two outcomes if I were present: Charles would be dead or myself. He was in my house, my fortress. My mind is boggled and afire.

I had to leave my business for the first time that I can remember in a very long time. My staff took over and maintained business as usual, even though they were up in arms. I had to take a sedative to calm my thoughts. I will leave it, first of all, in the Lord's hands and in the law's hand tonight.

The word is out like wildfire. I can only assume that he has crossed the Savannah River and fled this county. There is a bounty on his head and that is all I can say on this matter, Journal. I actually pray that the bounty is never paid. It is not common in this community, even in the Blue Light District, that we bring harm to one another. There is usually a stabbing or two over a woman or drunkenness, but that is about it. We have some domestic violence, but rarely.

Usually, the violence comes from someone visiting our community or just passing through. Charles could not have gotten too far at this point. All eyes are out. I will give Sarah time to rest before I talk to her. I will just console her for now. She is holding up well, though, under the circumstances, and the doctor said she will be fine. He recommended rest for a few weeks. It will be hard to keep Sarah Beale still, though. Maybe I will send her away to one of our getaway havens.

———

Other than the eventful day with Sarah Beale, it is a beautiful Augusta day. Sarah is alive, which makes it even more beautiful. I can smell all the native flowers of Georgia. The humidity is okay, and the mosquitoes are at a low. Because of this climactic day, I have been able to take a break from the normal routine of my life, unfortunately, at the expense of Sarah. Charles must have been in a crazed state of mind to have entered my domain, my castle, my haven. He surely knew what the outcome would be had he been caught for performing this vicious act. Was he under the influence of the grape or the devil? Maybe it was both. I fear neither, especially when it comes to Sarah or my family.

There have been many rumors about the reason for this attack. None have come directly to me. I will take this time to reflect on the many issues I have neglected to address because of my time-consuming business. I am so used to only the dealings inside the walls at my gentlemen's and ladies restaurant; it would fill twenty novels if I chose to write about it. Hmm, Journal, make note of that on my things-to-do list.

There I go again, drifting. I must not be consumed by rumors on the matter of Sarah's attack. I have always been able to maintain success because I keep a level head. I always get the facts first then react accordingly. This is the first time I have been adversely affected by outside forces that I couldn't control right at my doorstep. This is totally new to me. As I think about what happened, it feels like a fictional story I have read. This has certainly been a reality check. I believe I needed this.

I have not heard the creatures of the night in a long time. I am used to orders being placed, laughter, billiard balls clanking, and the smell of ale, cognacs, and whiskey. The smell of my delicacies, open conversations on subjects of clandestine nature, cooks in the kitchen, and bartenders entertaining. These are the sounds I am accustomed to, which equate to my success. I have not thrown a dart, played croquet, played a good bridge hand or whist, read a novel fully, looked at a sunset, relaxed to the crackling sound of a fire, or listened to a good joke—though I am always telling them—in a long time. Even in church on Sundays, my mind is involved in things other than the Lord at times, even though I do worship Him, contrary to what others believe.

Every day that I wake up is a good day. It is another day that the Lord has allowed me to get down on my knees and pray. He has been my strength, my fortress. All of the powers I possess are direct gifts from God and no other. Many say I am possessed with self and greed or that I have an evil presence. I am possessed with the insight given to me by my Lord God and Savior. He was persecuted as well but my suffering is no comparison to His sacrifice and the crown of thorns that He bore. I am a humble servant. I am a vessel and He is my captain. I am a passenger on His ship and He has allotted me a ticket of passage.

I am burning rags now that the midnight pests are upon the night. I have yet to partake in my mint julep, though the aroma is so enticing. I am on the upper veranda and I hear someone stirring about. The night is unusually still. Either I have blocked it out, or the community awaits below for me to unveil my actions in regard to Charles. I have no plans but to reflect and relax, if that is at all possible under these circumstances. The other part of me is present, observing my every thought with great concern. This time he is without question, as if only present to console me. The night is so still. I feel so blessed. The night's breeze just turned my journal to an empty page. I will take that as a sign to retire and say good-night to myself and the one who watches over me.

I was awakened early with news of the whereabouts of Sarah Beale's assailant. I have eyes and ears that stretch far. I am told that he crossed the Savannah River. They say he acts as if he has the fever or that nasty man's disease. They say he is as rabid as a coon.

I had already been told that he had made advances toward my hired help and my Sarah. That was the reason I'd dismissed him from employment. I even took the time to explain to him that I understood his desires, but not to let that rule his thoughts. I gave him a chance to redeem his emotions, but when he said he could not do so, I dismissed him. He said that he understood, but he denied coming on to Sarah.

I had asked Sarah previously if this had ever occurred, and she said only with the help. I knew him to be the flirtatious sort but not crazy enough to try and sow his seeds on my land. I also know that Sarah is one to try and keep the peace because of what my reaction might be. She said that the help came to her in counsel.

I am a man of high honor. Many are loyal to me and will take action upon this unfortunate soul without counsel from me. They take offenses against me personally. I have no time for scandal. Even though I am human and not without sin, I try to live a righteous life, regardless of others' opinions. I am just a no-nonsense type of man.

CHAPTER 34
FINDING INNER PEACE

Dear Journal,

I enjoy humor and peaceful thoughts above all other emotions in my life, not to say that negative emotions do not sometimes prevail. I am a businessman first, and I do not need conflict of emotions to interfere with my goals and dreams. I believe in harmony. Live and let live. I believe this world would be in better shape if we all had that understanding. It goes without saying. We live in a world of haves and have nots, which perpetuates turmoil. I always preach for people to reach for the stars but in the meantime, be accepting of their present situations until they can implement their goals. Truth is, as I always say, we tend to want what others have, but it is not our own truth.

You need to know what truly will make you happy. You can only find that through discovery of self, but you must first know that you are an individual who is not to be grouped with any other soul on this planet. Don't lose that present moment you are experiencing. Whether it is a negative or positive situation or a combination of both, you must evaluate it and progress. Sometimes, just standing still can be progress. Within your circumstances always lies the truth, the truth to your inner peace.

Even though it may seem that I am one of those persons I am referring to, it is not so. I set daily levels of achievement. I plan for the future, but I actually live one day at a time because tomorrow is not promised. This has proven to be quite a successful formula for me.

This newfound freedom has confused both sides. Most of those who have had to free souls take it as defeat. Those who have been freed are either confused, unknowledgeable, or scared, broken souls, afraid to grab ahold of this golden opportunity the Lord has given the world. I, being a businessman, find it beneficial to both sides. A happy worker is a more productive worker.

I may give more monetary compensation, but I will recoup it tenfold because of the output of production. My staff will produce under this method, and it also gives me inner peace, knowing that I am being fair and bettering someone's life. I am still in control but that is not the main objective. If it is, you will lose sight of the fact that that which makes you can also break you. I am not trying to control souls like other men have done, self-appointing themselves as demigods. That is the problem. My kin from another time tells me that the future entails controlling souls and thoughts. Many men are followers of other men's thoughts and not those of their own.

An employer is supposed to control the manner in which he conducts his business and the manner in which he wants you to think about doing his bidding; however, you do not have to let him control your thoughts. You can do both and be more productive to yourself and your employer. You will find peace in this mindset. Let one man's dream perpetuate your dream. If one man can do it, so can you with your dream. Never stop dreaming. A negative plus a negative is a negative result. Deal with your present situation and use it as a stepping stone. Maybe this is where you are supposed to be, but keep honing what you're doing and be the best at it.

Everyone may not want to be the boss. Everyone is not destined to be the boss. You are the boss and master of your soul, the controller of your inner peace. No one can take your inner peace away from you unless you allow them to do so. A man can physically peel back your scalp, but it will never divulge your thoughts.

Many have gone to their graves, gasping from the end of a rope. I have seen the peace on their faces as they took that last breath. I was saddened to witness these atrocities, but it gave me great relief when I saw the look of inner peace being released. I could tell that they were finally, truly free at last. Death has taught me many things.

These people of power concentrate on self instead of how all can benefit. This has been a factor since the beginning of time. It is amazing that we have progressed as the human race (and I use the term "progressed" loosely) because we continually transgress. We take five steps forward, only to take four steps back. It is amazing that we have not self-destructed.

Many nights, I ask myself if we are on the path of annihilation. Every chance I get, I read history and try not to repeat destruction. There are others who share the same mindset but few are heard.

The Bible states, "On the seventh day, God rested and what He saw was good." Even I rest in my own way and I always sit back at the end of the day and see what is good. There is always some good, but we tend to put the negative first when we look back. Put good first and the bad won't seem as bad. The good is that you made it to the end of the day. Every day that I awake is a good day, another that I have lived.

I try to share my philosophy with others, Journal, and I try to be an example. They listen but they do not take the time to comprehend. Every man has a story to tell. The saying goes, "You can lead a horse to water, but you can't make him drink."

I know there is one who does listen, understand, and share the same thoughts as myself, but he only comes to me in dreams or semi-consciousness. The one who sits on the edge of his chair or most times sits at my feet, listening to every word that I speak. I ask him his name but then I always awaken. Maybe it is myself I dream of in another consciousness. I am not always in a tiresome state when I write to you, Journal. He is becoming so real, to the point that I can almost touch him. Is it my inner soul that I reach out and attempt to touch?

He sometimes shares words of wisdom, hope, and guidance that he says he has received from me. I am still trying to figure that one out. He is so refreshing to me because I know that he not only listens but understands me and appears to wait to apply my wisdom. He gives me hope that all of my thoughts shared with you, Journal, will not be in vain. Once again, another beautiful night. I find my peace with ink on paper. You can find peace in the strangest places.

Inner peace is, first of all, recognizing that you have a soul that was bequeathed to you and no other possesses it. This is the start to finding yourself. You are a unique creation. Your destiny is that of no other, unless you choose to duplicate another's reality, and even then, it is not truly yours.

A mother knows all the differences of her child as well as the Creator does. She loves all her children equally but in different ways. The key is that they are all her children, born of her womb. We are all children of this earth and God's creation. We are all created from the same love of the great Father. The one who comes to me from another time tells me that he weeps as he witnesses the transgressions of the world. I weep as well. He feels that the burden of sin is placed on his shoulders, even though he knows he cannot save the world. We shed tears together, knowing that all do not share our awareness.

Imagine if we all knew the power that we have within us to do our part to make this world a utopia. It was like this in the beginning, and God has promised that it will be like this in the end. My question is whether all the needless hate, war, and atrocities are necessary, needed to reach salvation. God gave us free will, so I believe He has allowed us to go through these transgressions. We can eliminate all of this strife and cut through the red tape and assist our Father in expediting total harmony among the human race. I know that we can because it is written. Our destiny is in our hands. Denounce the evil one and there will be no Armageddon because he will have no soldiers to fight a war. My kin tells me that the war we fight is within. The evil ones are in minority, yet they rule. Wake up, my people of the human race! I beg of you.

I pray all the time for peace around the world, peace for all men and peace in our hearts. There can be no peace if there is no peace in your heart, regardless of adversities. We are worth our weight in gold. Let the light shine through, the light of love and equality.

I know my philosophy is not of a popular vote. It probably will be many years before this way of thought will be the norm. I do not deny my heritage. I am well respected by those in power but less respected by those of color. Why is that? We are our own worst enemy at times. We don't see that this is the way they want us to be. Like many great leaders of war, the object is to divide and conquer.

I have been classified in records as a Negro as well as a mulatto. My Negro brother dislikes me because I only serve Europeans. They, as well, have services that only the European uses. They work with me and are treated as equals other than the fact that I am the proprietor. They have many ill names for me.

They must not be mad at me because my brother and I had the insight to create such a business. They do not understand that I serve as somewhat of an ambassador to their own cause. Respect is given to me greatly and respect and awareness of the capabilities of men of color is projected to them as well. Yes, it is a fact that whites favor fairer skinned Negroes, but they respect the services offered from the darker skinned Negroes as well.

There are those who limit themselves instead of using me as an example of hope and how to succeed in these days. Most see the color of their skin as a drawback. We live in experimental times, where, in essence, a man is judged by what he can produce that will be an aid to the progression of the European success. Most just don't know any better, but I explain to them the mindset of the European in this region.

We will still be kept in our place, but we can advance covertly instead of being radicals with closed minds of hatred. Mind you, I do understand that they have lived through great atrocities and have been victims of a society that has made them bitter. I, too, have gone through experiences. I learn from them and move on. They, too, must learn to be manipulative and channel their bitterness into their own sweetness.

I agree that, at times, you have to bring the axe handle out of the shed. I more so believe that using intelligent thought and organization is a wiser approach to freedom. Every day, I hear of new weapons and methods to control the defiant ones. If we do not unite, there will be a day of Armageddon in which no one wins. There is going to be a time when we all have to come together. I believe that we are all responsible for our destiny as a human race. There cannot be a dictatorship; it must become democracy. We must share each other's beliefs and we must find a common ground.

My kin from another time shares visions with me of what is to come. These visions are similar to how I was raised, where whites, American Indians, Scottish, and other races wed without provocation from a hate group. He wants me to know that this merging of races can exist. He shows me that even in his day, people in interracial marriages become victims of racism. This comes from both sides of the union.

South Carolina and Georgia were free states until the king sent his dissident, bottom-of-the-barrel people to this region. As a result, slavery expanded to other southern states. Prior to that, just land owners and those with their own trades worked for these people. Georgia was a free state but became a proving grounds for slavery.

There was a social order and people accepted their existence. Doctors, blacksmiths, builders, and inventors, were and still are of many denominations and live fair lives. Things have changed because of outside influences and other cultures seeing the opportunity to capitalize on the naiveté of the less fortunate.

I pray that the one who visits is not just an entity, but a vessel sent to me to enlighten him on the plans of the ones who rule. He tells me that he knows of similar plans. We are all equal in God's eyes, with different purposes in life. One cannot live without the other. Life should not be defined by a dominant group of the wealthy.

I hope I have empowered him with some facts and wisdom to make a difference in his times. He tells me that he is writing a book on my enlightenment. He tells me that he, too, is drawn into a black hole, where I come to him in his writings and his pen is totally taken over by my thoughts. He says that my spirit engulfs his body and I am the reason for his book. He says that he goes into a trance, same as I do, when he is present. He tells me that he comes back the next day to see what has been written. He knows that it was my pen in his hand that unveiled these truths. He is as mystified as I am about our relationship.

I know I am starting to sound a little mystical here. With that, Journal, I will say good night and good morning. The wind has again blown to an empty sheet, so I will take that as a sign to retire. Until we meet again, peace unto me and mankind. Either we come together as a human race, or we will expire as a dying race.

CHAPTER 35
KIN FROM ANOTHER TIME

Dear Journal,
My kin from another time has finally come to me clearly. He has told me that he is, in fact, my great-great-grandson—second great! He has shared this with me because he fears he may lose connection with me on this spiritual journey of enlightenment. He has also shared with me that he does not want to alter the future by joining souls with me. So it has not all been a dream or manifestation of fatigue, as I had guessed. He has stressed to me that his mission is to find out what happened to our family lineage. He tells me that he and his newfound cousin, Krystal, have pieced a lot of it together.

My kin from another time has expressed to me that there will be lawsuits filed after my son, Lexius Jr.'s, demise that would make my skin crawl because of his decision to denounce his family, just as I had spoken of, Journal. My worst nightmare comes true. He believes this to be why my family never knew our tree. I am saddened to know that my estate and legacy were not passed down. He promises me that his legacy will be passed on and my estate does not matter. My legacy is worth its weight in gold to him and his family, especially his mother.

I had purposely hidden my assets so there would be no bickering over my estate in the event this did occur. I also made provisions so if one of my sons betrayed my wishes, my assets would skip generations and be given to those more deserving. I guess this did not happen. He tells me that the estate will be lost to treachery but not to worry because the family turns out okay financially. The bloodline means much more than any monetary factors.

The regret is that his mother, Mary Elizabeth, the daughter of Mattie Lee, who is the product of the union between Hattie and my son Lexius Jr., has no family history to pass on. He tells me that my son, Harper, did not denounce his heritage. One of the limbs of my family tree is Gertrude, the daughter of Harper and my grand-daughter, who will marry a King and keep the family strong, though with a missing link.

Gertrude's family migrates to California. Lexius Jr.'s estate is challenged by his daughter, Mattie Lee, and son, Hugh Henson. He tells me that he has the actual case on paper. My second great grandson shares with me that he met my grandson, Hugh, on one occasion but never met his grandmother, Mattie Lee. He remembers a well-dressed man of great stature. Hugh Henson married twice but produced no offspring. When Hugh died, my great-great-grandson and his mother, Mary, traveled to New York to bury him. It was found that the family of Hugh's wife, Pearl, owned a city block in Ybor City in Tampa, Florida.

All that Mary received were two crisp one hundred-dollar bills that were in Hugh's pocket when he died.

Liz, as Hugh called Mary, was very dear to him. He knew no other blood relatives from his uncle Harper's side. If he did, he did not divulge this information to her. He, too, kept secrets of our past. Hugh is the one who passed on the portrait of me to Mary. Hugh took Mary to the house of a woman of European descent, where she was not allowed to participate in the conversation. This is where Mary was given the portrait of me with Sarah Beale. The picture that my second great grandson tells me about appears to have become the portal to our union and his travel to my present, like a sort of time travel device. I remember that portrait quite well. Mary was told that I was her grandfather, but in reality, I am her great grandfather. Mary believes that the woman was the sister of her natural father.

My second great grandson tells me that he and his mother located the whereabouts of her father and they were about to travel to Augusta to make the discovery. Two weeks before their trip, her alleged father passed away. Her father was believed to be a man of means by the last name Grey, from Waynesboro, Georgia. He says his mother tells of remembering a man who made it a point to come by and spend time with her on occasion. Through her observation of the conversation between her Uncle Hugh and her alleged father's sister, Mary deduced the identity of her natural father; however, she has never been able to verify her suspicions. So many souls have been separated because of race. This saddens me, but at the same time, it tells me that I have two family members who will not rest until this puzzle is pieced together. He tells me that it is more than that; all of his siblings, his mother, Krystal, his nephews, and nieces are doing their part to unit this family.

Krystal, being of the same generation and cousin of my second great grandson, Craig, is the Harper offspring from Gertrude King. Oh, my goodness, I just called his name ... Craig! This is the first time this was revealed to me. Journal, I must take a moment here.

It appears that my family tree turns out to be a well-written mystery. It boggles my mind how many other families are going to experience the same. Craig tells me that his mother tells him that she can remember going to a restaurant where her mother, Mattie Lee, worked, but it was owned by another family by the name of Bates. She did not know of any family connection.

Craig tells me that Mary's uncle, P.R, to which I entrusted much, took good care of her. Craig tries not to confuse me with a lot of detail about future outcomes. He tries not to disturb me with the fact that my legacy no longer exists, but I am a wise man and I can read in between the lines and tell that my lineage was stifled until he traveled into my dreams.

Craig tells me that there are many unsolved mysteries in our tree, but he is getting closer to solving them with the help of family and

Krystal. All he started out with were photographs of three family members that tie him to his mulatto background: Mattie Lee, Hugh Henson, and myself. I commend him on his dedication with such limited resources.

I guess I have passed on by his present time, or else I am as old as Methuselah! Craig speaks of new technology, where one can find his ancestry through a screen of some sort. He also talks of wanting my recipes because he brags of being a great saucier and chef. He wishes he had my personalized china to complement his exquisite cuisines and wonders where my silverware and linens went. He thinks Mattie Lee's husband sold all the silverware that was endowed to her.

Craig tells me that he does not want for much in his life but for the desire to know his history. He thanks me for being able to share a part of me and says he now understands his extravagant cravings and rich taste, even though he is on a beer budget. I see that he has my humor as well. One thing that he says he doesn't thank me for is his receding hairline, but he laughs.

Craig tells me what prompted his ultimate journey into my world. The crossover occurred when his brother, Nathaniel, passed away. As they gathered at Nathaniel's birth home, his oldest sister, Denise, discussed the mysterious photograph, which was a photo of me. Craig said Denise looked into a looking glass called a computer, which he tried to explain to me, but it sounds like witchcraft, though he assures me that he is a Christian and the computer is technology. He and Denise typed in my name and suddenly appeared my claim to fame—my legacy! As Craig sat in the room with his siblings, Uncle Roscoe, and Aunt Alice, many jokes were thrown to him in jest because they had always teased him for being a dreamer, who no one often believed, although they knew he had been tested and was found to have the IQ of a genius. He said they teased him because of the receding hairline we both share.

Craig tells me that from that point in his life, strange, dreamlike happenings began to occur, including being transported back in time, to my time and my life. He also tells me about the discovery of my sons, Lexius Jr. and Harper, through this looking glass computer. He tells me that was when he met Krystal as well. They would find out they were cousins, and this would lead to the fact that Mary had family other than the Rush/Webber union. Now, mind you, Mary is in her nineties and is just now finding the other side of her family, though her paternal side remains undiscovered. Craig tells me that Mary had just found her sister, Michelle, only eight years ago, after a fifty-year separation. It appears that this meeting opened the floodgates to my immortality.

Craig tells me that he knows it was my restless soul and God and his brother, Nathaniel's, intervention that brought about this vessel of closure and enlightenment. He knows that Krystal is being used as well. This knowledge gives me peace as I grow old. I believe it to be true. I tire now, and I am up in age, but I will come back to this incredible journey if my body allows me to. Until me meet again, Journal. I bid you good morning.

CHAPTER 36
CRAIG'S WORLD

Dear Journal,
I have dreams now that I have passed on into Craig's world, and now our roles have reversed. I now come into his world as he did mine. I now become an eager student as he was. What a strange time it is. It is as he'd described his life in the future, but one thousand times multiplied with the technology he had shared with me.

I am quick to learn, but these future times are incredible! What is really strange is that I had these visions as a child in my dreams. I suppose they were dreams. I am now wearing the shoes of my great-great-grandson as he tries to explain his time travel with me. I am in awe. The end of my days on this earth must draw near.

I am able to now see Craig writing about me. I call to him, but he does not see or hear me. What he writes about are my thoughts that were only privy to you, Journal. He is literally writing my thoughts. I know I sound like a crazed man, but I know that I am of sound mind, just old! Is it possible that he has discovered my entrusted confidant? Has he discovered you, Journal?

What kind of witchcraft or divine intervention is this? I see him so clearly now, even more so than when he visited me in my dreams. Now, I am visiting him? What is it that I am experiencing? It is totally mind boggling and incredible! I hope that no one will find this journal now. They will surely have grounds to contest any written will I have left behind. It would be more the journal of a mad man that that of enlightenment. I am laughing somewhat but serious at the same time, because I know it to be true.

He writes by candlelight, as I did, and late in the morning hours, while all others are asleep. There is a light in the background that is powered by what appears to be electricity. He sits in his car shelter, with man's best friend roaming about in the dark backyard of his home. It is so real that I can smell the cognac in his glass that he is too preoccupied to enjoy because of his intense writing. I can smell an ale in his beer mug, poured from a brown bottle that he never drinks from as well. This is so crazy because it is a replica of how I write to you, Journal! His cigar reeks as one dipped in cognac, much like the ones sold to my richest clients. This at least tells me that he is of means, I hope. He burns incense as well.

He has the same hairline as me, but he appears to be younger than his half-balding head indicates. He wears spectacles, as I do, though very few have seen me with them. He also writes in print, as I do, not in cursive. The night is very still right now in his world. I hear crickets and sounds of motors in the distance.

Maybe he did find my china, secret chest, and silverware, because I count five automobiles that I have never seen before. His estate appears to be comfortable from the outside view. He smokes a very skinny cigar, though, as if his tobacco is limited, but I can tell by the aroma that it is of fine quality, the same that I am accustomed to. He writes as the world sleeps and I can tell that he is tired, too, but he cannot put his pen down.

He uses a unique quill. It produces ink without dipping into a well. His thoughts are written down as rapidly as the ink flows out of it. He even blows the smoke from his cigar into his snifter of cognac, like a fog over the land before he sips it. Is this me in another life? He is interrupted by one who appears to be another, younger one of my descendants. Why is he up this late? I do not know.

CHAPTER 37
KEEP HOPE ALIVE

Dear Journal,
A lot of my wealthy clients are dying off. Unfortunately, only a few of them have passed on to their offspring the experience of dining at my fine restaurant. The rich usually kept it secret, under their hats of experiences that are contrary to their teachings. This is not good for business. It is as well that my children have not followed me into business. I have never enforced any wishes for them to continue my legacy. I have encouraged them to be their own bosses and have their own businesses, but it does not appear that this is going to happen. Perhaps I made life too easy for them. I wish, though, that they would have carried on the business that my brother and I created.

Perhaps this is why a higher power has allowed me to enter into a relationship with Craig, my kin from another time. Most of his interests appear to be mirror images of mine, hallelujah! He also appears to be one who will take risks in the business world. This would make sense as to why we have been drawn together. His world seems to be very fast paced. There are many who seek riches, whereas in my times, wealth was limited to bloodlines and passed down from old money.

I now have the privilege of seeing his thoughts. Craig has so many, but no one backs his dreams. Maybe this is my legacy. Maybe it is my purpose to aid him in his endeavors, using my life as a guide. He appears to be a highly intelligent individual, and many have followed his guidance. He relishes in sharing knowledge. Not all heed his advice, only to find out later that he was the wise one.

I gave much to others at no cost and he tells me that he did as well. He and I both want to save the world. We both understand the constraints that are placed upon us. We do not use these restraints as a deterrent but as fuel to fire up the masses, or at least the ones who will listen, the ones who are wise enough to hear. It is like looking into a mirror as I observe him. It is so fascinating. Is it a dream? Have I passed on? Is this purgatory? Is this the stage between redemption or damnation?

I smile because I see the same zealousness for life in him. Craig does not believe in limitation of one's imagination or expectations. Unfortunately, he does not have the backing or support of those close to him. This sounds familiar to my situation, with the exception of my father and Charles. My mother backed me but was very conservative; he tells me that the same is true for him. He loves his family over any other thing in his life. His love for mankind sometimes blinds him from the hate that other men have for him. He tells me that his mother has continually shared with him that people take his kindness for weakness.

He confesses that he can see that to be true, but he has the same philosophy as me, that you should never give more than you can afford to lose. He is like a flame that moths are attracted to. They wish they had his courage but are leery of investing in his dreams. That is why I waited for no man to invest in my dreams.

It appears that he celebrates the success of others. Sometimes, this comes at his own loss. Many have called me a dreamer. This is why I do not sleep at night. Craig's thoughts, too, won't rest. I pray that he does not totally duplicate my persona. One thing I regret is that I didn't take enough time to smell the flowers and the aromas in my kitchen.

CHAPTER 38
ENDING

Dear Journal,
This is becoming very difficult for me to understand. This is the joint experience of myself and my great-great-grandson. He came to me first as a child, seeking knowledge on his grandfather's knee. Then he listened very attentively, short of writing it down on a pad, in my presence. Now, I am able to observe his world. It seems that he doesn't have the same fervor as when I'd first come into his existence. He now shares with me his anguishes about mankind and how he feels he will not be able to change the human race to unite and become one.

There are many naysayers in his presence, but I still see a resilience in him. He has made many rich, but none return the favor. I can tell that he is like me because he does not give to receive. But he would like a "thank you" here and there. That would be sufficient payment to him.

He doesn't care if the world knows his name. He feels obligated to continue his dream of unification of the human race. I assume that I have long passed. How can I contribute to his success? I see for certain now that he spends long hours writing about me, sacrificing many things during this mission he has taken on.

He is so proud of my existence. How can I reciprocate and let him know of my appreciation for his existence? He has so much love for me. I want to sit down and talk to him. Hopefully, I have when he came to me in my dreams.

Like I said, Journal, this is becoming so complicated. It is like a Shakespeare play, where you have to pay close attention or you lose the plot. I had become comfortable with him coming into my existence. Now, all of a sudden, I have been thrust into his world. Hold on to your hat, Journal!

What is the purpose of this transference? He has already written that he comes into my world and time. We had come to a point where we had formed a true relationship and not that of a dream. At that point, I was whisked into his world.

What is going on, Journal? Am I about to leave this place? Am I mad? I enjoyed being a mentor to him. Now, what is my role in his world? I am not able to interact with him as he did in my world. We finally had physical conversation when he came to me last.

I have yet to be able to alarm him of my presence in his world. Yes, I know this is craziness, Journal. I wish you could write a page so I could understand what is transpiring. It is time now, Journal, for me to terminate our relationship. Is it time, now, for me to edit his writings, his story of my journal? Is it time for me to give him closure? What is it he wants? I feel like screaming at this point!

Am I able to live up to the man that he portrays me to be? The facts that he has written about me are accurate, but am I worthy of the story that he writes? Am I truly a historical person of note? Fame has never been my intention and neither that of Craig, as far as I can tell. He writes this story, not for fame, but to serve as an enlightenment, a guideline to the world to find peace, love, and the realization of one race, the human race. The love of his mother's peace seems to weigh as equally as his love of all God's children.

Craig has truly conveyed the feelings and philosophies that I was unable to share with the people of my time. I can only imagine what he was feeling while being engulfed in the travesties of my era. He shared with me the relief he felt that he was not alone in his thoughts of unification of all.

I will have to destroy this journal after the last entry and pray that he truly transcribed my life. If I were another person reading what I've written, I would undoubtedly think it was written by a diseased man. Journal, please acknowledge that I am not crazy. If you do respond to me, then I definitely know that I have lost my mind.

I am very tired now. I feel a very heavy sleep overtaking me. I feel this is where we part ways, Journal. Thank you for being there for me. Live on!

Until we meet again. As Shakespeare once said, "We are all actors, placed upon a stage." What role will you play, Craig? What role did I play?

What Happens Is

What happens is ... a brother, sister, cousin marrying and never knows

What happens is ... a brother, sister, uncle, auntie, cousin killing one another

What happens is ... telling the beggar to get out of your face

What happens is ... family robbing you

What happens is ... the segregation of family, the deterioration of a society, walking around dead with many unanswered questions, confused

What happens is ... not knowing why you feel and why you do the things you do because of those black holes in your life

– C.E.R

EPILOGUE

Lexius's worst nightmare did come to pass. I did not have it in my heart to share this with him during my time travel relationship with him. If there is a heaven, and I believe there is, he knows this by now. Lexius Jr. would go on to disinherit his Negro wife, my great grandmother, Hattie, as well as his two mulatto children, Hugh and Mattie Lee Henson. He left Uncle P.R. out of the will also. It was believed that Lexius Henson Jr. was not in the right state of mind. Lexius Jr. had his attorney controlling his inheritance from Lexius Henson Sr. Lexius Jr. raised both of his children and was present in the household along with his wife, Hattie. Hugh was present at the time of his father's death. Mattie was in Waynesboro, Georgia with their mother, who had taken ill and passed shortly thereafter. Lexius Jr. passed shortly after Hattie.

Hugh and Mattie Lee sued for rights to Lexius Jr.'s estate, all the way to the Georgia Supreme Courts. The case showed that his estate was worth only fifty dollars, yeah right! The truth was that Lexius Jr. had great wealth, left to him by Lexius Sr., but its value had been manipulated by his attorney, Mr. Wolf. Oh, what an appropriate name for this attorney. Mr. Wolf was the attorney general of Georgia at the time of the lawsuit. It appears that Lexius Jr. was not in the right state of mind when working with this attorney, with whom he had a very close relationship that was not clearly defined. Mr. Wolf had also been an attorney for Lexius Sr.

It was necessary for Mr. Wolf to deem that Lexius Jr.'s estate was willed solely to him because assets had been hidden and not presented to the court. Lexius Sr. was very shrewd with his money, and records showed that Lexius Sr. was worth $20,000 in cash assets, which is equivalent to $800,000 to $1,000,000 today. Lexius Sr. made provisions for both of his sons, whom he cherished so dearly. Lexius Jr. also denied that he knew the whereabouts of his brother, Harper, and stated that they did not have a relationship.

The big question is why would the case go all the way to the Georgia Supreme Court for fifty dollars? The transcript of the entire case is published in these pages. Take the time to read every line of this documented case, and you tell me what happened. This case is an example of how so many families of color were disinherited by the Wolfs of the world. So many of us were robbed of our true family lineage and the wealth that came along with it.

In this case, Lexius Jr. speaks with negativity about the color of his dark-skinned Negro wife. The testimonies given on behalf of the defendants and the plaintiffs were by some of the most prominent lawyers and individuals in Georgia at that time. Why was it so important to bring in the big guns? One of the reasons was because Lexius Sr. ran with the big guns and there was much at stake. I promise my great-great-grandfather that I will do my utmost to reveal the skullduggery that occurred in my next book. In reading this case, it is obvious that injustice prevailed.

A positive take away from the trial was the opportunity for me to read the intelligent responses of my great-great-uncle, P.R., my great uncle, Eric, and my grandmother, Mattie Lee. The aforementioned were unshakable in their testimony. Eric was only nineteen and Mattie Lee was only twelve at the time. They removed Uncle P.R. from the stand quickly and I know he had his pistol in his pocket. Their testimonies assure me of the accuracy of all the stories my mother used to tell me about Uncle P.R. and Uncle Son. It gives me so much validity.

There is nothing I can do about the past and this case, but I, and you as well, can learn from it. It is not about the money for me, but about revealing the ways of the wicked. The inheritance would have just been a bonus. Maybe in the search for my heritage, I will find two treasures.

So many African Americans have had land willed to them, but most have defaulted because of taxes. How many of you does this apply to? I implore all of you who relate to this to secure that land by any means necessary. Within that land lies many great secrets and much blood, sweat, and tears. I have lost land from my father's side, which at one time had a very profitable mill on it. I have numerous stories of close friends who have had the same experience.

Our forefathers, in some cases, died for their legacies to be passed on to us. I guess many of our ancestors are rolling over in their graves in unison and singing the same spiritual hymn. My grandfather on my father's side never said much, but the words he did share were of infinite wisdom, including the importance of owning land. Granddaddy Pete said, "That is the only definite thing you can count on that will always be there."

I don't believe in dwelling or living in the past. The point to be made here is to acquire new land and hold onto what was bequeathed to you. We usually end up fighting over the land and liquidate for pennies on the dollar, meaning that no one profits. Then the next thing you hear is that a strip mall or something very profitable has been placed on your land. I repeat, your land! Secure the land and pass it on. We pass on nothing but debt and families fighting at funerals.

Talk to your elderly family members. The riches lie in their mere existence. Their survival is of far greater value than any plot of land or gold bars. Richness is in the family's soul. We are running around with no history, no past, and no dreams of which our ancestors prayed we would achieve.

I do not just speak of the African American race. If we, as a human race in America, knew what our ancestors went through, we would know that most ethnic denominations were discriminated upon. Much was taken from all by a few who were in control. As long as we are fighting amongst ourselves, we will never know our worth—conquer and divide.

We have been isolated and driven to think that each race is alone in its plight. If we could only raise our level of awareness to see that we all want the same things, together, as a human race, we could achieve a Utopia! Oh, my Lord, what would happen if we opened our eyes and saw that we are all in the same boat of life? I'll tell you what would happen, there would be love of your brothers and sisters, no matter what color, and economic equality. The current cipher was designed by those that have, to keep us have nots confused and self-intertwined for survival of self. Individuals cannot survive alone, but a human race, together, can be eternal.

FROM THE AUTHOR

I promised that I would not bore you with historical dates and names, but it is now necessary to provide the names that developed these studies on polygenism, so you can do your own research on how this madness of racism was birthed on paper. Enslavement has been around from the beginning of time but was manifested for the needs of survival. Some cultures had the same ideology as the commission, but it was usually solely for religious purposes.

Get your pencil and pad out, and I will be brief so you will not lose sight of Lexius

Henson's enlightenment. If you do take the time to research these people, it may give you a whole other perspective on your way of thinking as Lexius had provided.

———————

1857 - G. Gliddon/J. Nott - *Indigenous Races of the Earth*:

This book promoted the polygenic theory of blacks being inferior to whites. J. Nott was the first founder of the school of anthropology. In 1843, he stated that there were separate creations for human races. He goes on to say that blacks only existence was for slavery. Nott writes about other terms: monogenists vs. polygenists, religion, and science.

1791-1862 - Robert Knox - Leading international figure in the polygenic movement (Yes, it was a movement).

1744-1829 - Jean-Baptiste deLamarck

deLamarck was a naturalist, who, during the Enlightenment Period, combined evolution with behavioral and biological sciences. He found that physical and mental changes took place in tandems as humanity originated in the eighteenth century. He tried to form a synthesis of biology with physical and chemical phenomenon. This was the last grand scheme of the period. He was one of the first to coin the term "biology" to describe his scientific studies, which included the phylogenic tree. The phylogenic tree states that species are related in a hierarchy of descent.

Fifteenth and sixteenth century European nations tried to justify their right to riches. Many justified polygenism based on non-humanity of the other creations and judged them to be without souls. This belief led to the birth of anthropology three hundred years later.

The rise of polygenism was linked to continued discoveries of human diversity, which were: the American Indians on two continents, the Koi and San of South Africa, and the Melanesians. There existed much more diversification of races than they had expected. After these and other discoveries of races, the Europeans were disturbed because they believed there were only three races: the whites of Europe, the yellow people (Asians), and blacks (Africans).

1774 - *Sketches of the History of Man* by Lord Kames

Kames suggested that God created pairs within the human race, differing from each other both externally and internally. He wrote that God fitted these pairs for different climates and placed each pair in its proper climate. The peculiarity of each pair was preserved in its entirety as their descendants. He concluded that

196

racial variation occurred later as a divine punishment for the redemption of the Tower of Babel. As you read this book and other books on this subject, you will find that racism is just a culmination of ignorance.

The definition of the word "nigger": ignorant in the mind, incapable of logical thoughts. Unaware of one's being; absence of the mind; no thoughts.

If you get a chance to read some of the listed materials, you will instantly see the ones who were absent of the power of logic and thought. We tend to say that racism doesn't affect us, but it does. To all of my human race brothers and sisters who read this book, I implore you to understand that the few who rule the majority are illogical in thought. We continue to make them heroes of hierarchy. We must stop the chain of this rule and understand that we can become the majority rule. Most know the truth but are afraid to go against the stream. I am not trying to cause a mass revolt of the lands, a rejection of one's mindset. All of our lives can be raised to a higher understanding. We can achieve a peace of mind without the distractions of these mind-altering doctrines.

We are all being enslaved, whether you know it or not. It is time to free your mind and your soul. It is amazing that a few men have changed and controlled our lives to date. They are long gone and all of their theories have been proven wrong and untrue. Let these men rest in their graves and let us be reborn to the enlightenment that we are all of the same race, the human race. We have different missions, but we should all have the same common goal, to "love thy neighbor" and for all to be prosperous without the chains of racism.

I'd rather be what I am, a member of the Negro race, than to be able to claim membership with the most favored of any other race. I have always become angry when I have heard members of my race claiming rights and privileges or certain badges of distinction on the grounds of their race, regardless of their individual worth or attainments.

Lexius Henson Sr. enjoyed the highest respect and confidence of both races in Augusta because of his due diligence. His uncompromising hard work, ethics, wisdom, and worldly knowledge gave him great power and influence that enabled the two races to live together in harmony and peace. He changed the attitude of many other races towards the stereotypes of the Negro. He showed that one's self-worth determines the man, as Booker T. Washington expressed.

The mulatto race is an important inclusion in the foundation of America. From the mulatto derived branches of all the facets of our lives and styles. There are those who lived the life of Europeans and those who fought through the struggle of being both white and black and being hated by both sides. John Hope is a perfect example. Lexius Henson is a perfect example as well, though many have said that he denounced his mixed heritage. Their journeys in life show that one needs to pursue his or her own dreams as well as the dreams of all mankind being united as the human race. Regardless of color, creed, or religious beliefs, we need to rise to a higher understanding of the Creator's plan. Even if you don't believe in the Creator, believe that we all came from the same tree and, therefore, are family.

Some accepted the prejudices and others revolted. Sometimes individuals were forced to become radical, but they were seeking their inner peace that they knew they were destined to purvey. The masses tried to portray a race war but that was not always the intent. History has shown that all races were involved in the unification of the human race through various struggles. From Gandhi to Huey P. Newton, their agendas were greater than race, and other powers will always try to mask their agendas with the falsehood that this was about a particular race.

There are those, to date, who have maintained local European heritage and fight against equality, even though they are of mixed heritage. They do whatever they can to mask their own identities. If there are gaps in your family's European heritage, then there is a great probability that you are one of the people I speak of. Embrace your roots and discover your rich lineage. History does not begin with the era of slavery. Modern times reflect and put emphasis on this period of time for the sole purpose of separatism. Do not fall into the trap of denying your inner peace. The ones who feed into this concept are the most dangerous ones of our time. You are still a beautiful creation, regardless of what the world has taught us.

Then there are those who have to prove their blackness. This is not a necessary act. Prove your worthiness, not your race. We can all see the color of our skin. That is the problem. It is not the color of the skin, but the strength of the soul that defines man. Remember, that is what you will be judged on. If you don't believe in judgment, I challenge you to do the right thing and you will feel the enlightenment of inner peace. There is no adulation in life that will compare to this.

It is time to let the skeletons out of the closet. There are those who plot separatism, whether it is for monetary gains or to prove a race to be superior. You must ask yourself during this period of enlightenment whether it makes a difference. You are accountable for yourself, not a particular race. The only race that counts is the human race, of which we all are.

There is another type that accepts and has embraced both sides of their heritage. This one is rare because society has taught us to choose one side over the other. The person who accepts both sides of his or her heritage is usually a very strong individual who embraces the love of all mankind. This person does not ride the fence and relates to the truth of both worlds. Both sides are within him or her, united as one, a human being from the human race, not that of an identity race or a piece of a puzzle. We are all necessary parts of the puzzle. This person is not puzzled by his or her identity and has nothing to prove but character.

The mulatto race has kept the seed and the power of America. It is the backbone and foundation of all walks of life, including some of our grand leaders of note. We all have long kept family secrets that no one bothers to explore. That deep secret is called the mulatto. We must embrace the fact that we are all from the same seed. We all have the same Father, whether you believe that is the ape or Adam.

Quotes of Inspiration and Thought

"I have learned that success is to be measured not so much by the position that one has reached in life but as by the obstacles which he has overcome while trying to succeed."

—Booker T. Washington

"Looked at it from this standpoint, I almost reach the conclusion that often the Negro boy's birth and connection with an unpopular race is an advantage, so far as real life is concerned. With few exceptions, the Negro youth must work harder and must perform his task even better than a white youth in order to secure recognition. But out of the hard and unusual struggle through which he is compelled to pass, he gets a strength, a confidence, that one misses when his pathway is comparatively smooth by reason of birth and race."

—Booker T. Washington

"The soul that is in me, no man can degrade. When told to sit in a baggage car and while one rider went to apologize, I responded that I am not the one to be degraded on account of this treatment, but those that inflicting this upon me are."

—Frederick Douglass

"When a great truth, once it gets abroad in the world, no power on earth can imprison it or prescribe its limits, or suppress it. It is bound to go on till it becomes the thought of the world."

—Frederick Douglass

"We have a journey to take and little time; we have ships to name and crews …"

—Henry Dumas

"I was there when the angel drove out the ancestor. I was there when the waters consumed the mountains."

—Bernard Dadie

"And they sold us like beasts and they counted our teeth … and they felt our testicles and they tested the luster or dullness of our skin."

—Cesaire

"(Joseph Cinque), leader of Amistad revolt - All the way from Africa to Georgia, I carried my sorrow songs. I made ragtime …"

—Langston Hughes

"I've been a victim. The Belgians cut off my hands in the Congo. They lynched me in Texas."

—Langston Hughes

"Oh, these cold, white hands manipulating, they broke us like limbs from a tree and carved Europe upon our African masks and made puppets …"

—Henry Dumas

"But the sweetness of labor is shared in the harvest …"

—Henry Dumas

"I want you to leap with me high into the sky until we see yellow trees …"

—Henry Dumas

"And this was this adult pain down deep in the soul because of which was laughter …"

—Feanyi Menkiti

AUTHOR'S ORIGINAL QUOTES

"Let one man's dream perpetuate your dream."

"I have a cellar of knowledge, most of which I cannot share because of the intoxication it may cause."

"Lack of common sense results in ignorance."

"Religion is a bandage placed on the wounds of slavery."

"I am not your enemy until we have cause to battle."

"If you have a soul, which you do, you have an opinion."

"It is much easier to hate a stranger than to hate a family member, which we all are."

"There is enough of the pie of life for all to share. All do not require a whole slice of it."

"Most would suffice with the crumbs of life or just being able to lick the pan."

"When the poorest is made glad, the richest would be made happier with their prosperity."

"It is to a point where all of America is mulatto."

"All that you are not let your brother or sister be. All that you have said, let me speak it, I am you."

"Those without a past are destined to a future without meaning."

"Without a mission, there is no urgency to be anywhere but the present. As a result, your destiny is predetermined by those who have a mission and are on a mission."

"My skin color has no distinction to men. I am not black, I am not white, nor am I bright, nor am I dark. I am a mulatto. I am you!"

"How can you be free if the only history you have is dated back to slavery."

"Don't try to change the world; just try to keep the world from changing you."

"I am not a root. I am not the trunk. I am not the tree … I am a season that has befallen upon me."

"We fight too many battles; let us just fight the war!"

"Sometimes just standing still can be progress."

"Either we come together as a human race, or we will expire as a dying race."

"Wait for no man to invest in your dreams."

"Prove your worthiness, not your race."

"It is not the color of your skin, but the strength of your soul that defines man."

Supreme Court of South Carolina,

CLERK'S OFFICE, COLUMBIA, S. C.

FILED FEB 25 1924

The State of South Carolina

IN THE SUPREME COURT

APRIL TERM—1924

Ex Parte HUGH HENSON AND MATTIE LEE HENSON, by their Guardian Ad Litem, Appellant,

In Re S. M. WOLFE, as Administrator with Will Annexed, and Beneficiary, under the last Will and Testament of Lexius P. Henson, deceased, Respondent.

APPEAL FROM ANDERSON COUNTY

HON. H. F. RICE, Judge.

CASE

J. M. PAGET, HOOD & HOOD,
Attorneys for Appellant.

BONHAM & ALLEN, A. H. DAGNALL,
Attorneys for Respondent.

STATEMENT

Lexius P. Henson, a negro, died in Augusta, Georgia, on or about the twenty-first day of November, 1920, leaving as his only heirs at law his two minor children, the Petitioners herein, of about twelve and eighteen years of age respectively, his wife having died prior thereto at the home of her mother in Waynesboro, Georgia. On the supposition that he had died inte-

SUPREME COURT

Ex Parte HUGH HENSON AND MATTIE LEE HENSON, Appellant.

state, one Paris R. Pryor, a brother-in-law of the deceased, was appointed administrator of his estate by the Courts of Richmond County, Georgia, and proceeded in the performance of his duties.

Thereafter, to wit, on April 18, 1922, Samuel M. Wolfe presented to the Probate Court of Anderson County a paper purporting to be the last will and testament of said Henson and filed petition praying that same be admitted to probate and that he be appointed administrator with the will annexed thereof, and the will was admitted in common form on the same date and letters of administration with the will annexed issued to him on his giving bond in the sum of four thousand ($4,000.00) dollars.

Thereafter on the _____ day of _____, 1923, the minor children by their Guardian ad Litem petitioned the Probate Court of Anderson County to require that the will be proven in solemn form, and thereupon the administrator, c. t. a., filed a petition in said Court on May 4, 1923, praying that he be permitted to prove the will in due form of law, and the Guardian ad Litem duly filed answer alleging lack of mental capacity; that the will was not executed in the manner prescribed by law for the execution of wills under the laws of South Carolina; that if Henson did sign the paper purporting to be his will that his execution thereof was induced and obtained by undue influence over him by the beneficiary therein, either consciously or unconsciously exerted, and by such misrepresentations or failure to give him information as to mislead him and prevent him from knowing and understanding the purport and effect thereof; that said instrument is null and void because in contravention of the laws of the State governing the relationship of attorney and client, and of the benefits that an attorney may take, obtain, or procure from his client, and invoking the protection of the Court.

SUPREME COURT

In re S. M. WOLFE, as Administrator, Respondent.

The cause was heard by the Probate Court on June 12, 1923, and thereafter he rendered his decree holding that the will was invalid and refusing probate thereof.

Notice of appeal therefrom was duly given by the Proponent herein, and both Proponent and Contestants served notice of issues to be submitted to the jury.

The appeal came to hearing before Judge Rice at the October term of Court on motion and argument by Proponent to refer the cause back to the Probate Court for alleged error of law and fact; but the Court refused the motion, stating that it should be tried de novo; and on the proposed issues for the jury being submitted to him at that time, he passed an order fixing the issues as proposed by Proponent, and refusing those proposed by Contestants.

When the cause was called for trial at the December term, Contestants moved that the following issue be also submitted to the jury, namely: "Did Lexius P. Henson reside in, or was he an inhabitant of, the County of Anderson, or of the State of South Carolina, at the time of his death?", and the motion was refused.

When the testimony was concluded, Proponent attorneys moved for a directed verdict in Proponent's favor on all of the issues submitted, which motion was granted, and in due time Appellants served notice of appeal to the Supreme Court.

ORDER OF OCTOBER 11, 1923, FIXING ISSUES:

"Upon an appeal herein to this Court from the Court of Probate, it is Ordered that there be a trial de novo by jury, and it is further Ordered and directed that the following questions of fact be submitted to the jury:

(1) Was the paper propounded as the will of Lexius P. Henson duly and legally executed?

(2) When said paper was executed did Lexius P. Henson have testamentary capacity?

SUPREME COURT

In Re HUGH HENSON AND MATTIE LEE HENSON, Appellant.

(3) Is the paper propounded the true last will and testament of Lexius P. Henson?

It is further ordered that the above case stand for trial at the next succeeding term of this Court.

TESTIMONY AND JUDGE'S STATEMENT IN GRANTING MOTION TO DIRECT VERDICT:

HERMAN BAILEY, a witness for the Plaintiff, being duly sworn, testified as follows:

DIRECT EXAMINATION by Gen. Bonham.

Q. What position do you hold in this County, Judge?

A. Probate Judge.

Q. What is the record which you have in your hand?

A. That's the Judgment Roll of the Estate of Lexius P. Henson.

Q. Will you please get from that roll the paper purporting to be the last will and testament of Lexius P. Henson. Is that it?

A. Yes, sir.

Gen. Bonham: We offer that in evidence, Your Honor, please.

Will introduced in evidence and marked exhibit A.

Mr. Hood: May Your Honor, please, I take it that they would have to prove the will, it wouldn't be competent to merely offer it in evidence, as I understand, in that way. They would have to prove the will by the attestation of the three witnesses.

Gen. Bonham: We understand that, but we can't prove it until we get it before the Court, but if my friend prefers, we will just have it marked for identification.

Mr. Hood: All right, sir.

Will marked C. V. S. for identification.

Mr. Hood: No questions.

J. L. SHERARD, a witness for the Plaintiff, being duly sworn, testified as follows:

SUPREME COURT

In Re S. M. WOLFE, as Administrator, Respondent.

DIRECT EXAMINATION by Gen. Bonham.

Q. Mr. Sherard, you are a practicing lawyer at this Bar, aren't you?

A. I am.

Q. How long have you practiced here?

A. Oh, about eighteen or twenty years.

Q. You were practicing here, then, in April of 1918?

A. I was.

Q. Did you know Lexius P. Henson?

A. Yes, sir, I knew him by name and knew him slightly; he was in the building very often.

Q. Mr. Sherard, I wish you would look at this paper and see if you signed it, if you witnessed it? (presenting same).

A. I witnessed this; this is my signature.

Q. Do you remember the occasion of the signing of that paper?

A. Yes, sir.

Q. It was on the date that it was affixed there, was it?

A. Yes, sir, I presume so; I didn't take any note of the date.

Q. Where was that paper signed?

A. It was signed in Mr. Wolfe's office.

Q. In what building is that—at that time?

A. Peoples Frank Building.

Q. Were your offices there, too, at that time?

A. Yes, sir, my office was two or three doors down towards the entrance from Mr. Wolfe.

Q. Who was present when the paper was signed, Mr. Sherard?

A. Dr. Shirley and Mr. W. J. Manos were there and witnessed it with me.

Q. Did you or not see the testator sign it?

A. Yes, sir, I saw him sign it.

Q. And did or not he sign it in the presence of you three witnesses?

In re HUGH BENSON AND MATTIE LEE HENSON, Appellant.

A. Yes, sir.
Q. And you signed it in his presence?
A. Yes, sir.
Q. And in the presence of each other?
A. Yes, sir.
Q. Mr. Sherard, do you know the handwriting of Mr. Wolfe, S. M. Wolfe?
A. Yes, sir, I know it very well.
Q. Is that paper in his handwriting?
A. No, this is not his handwriting.
Q. Mr. Sherard, what was the mental condition of the testator at the time that will was signed, in your opinion?
A. Well, I knew Henson very slightly, but in my opinion he had mental capacity to make a will.

CROSS-EXAMINATION by Mr. Rood.

Q. Mr. Sherard, was Mr. Wolfe present at the execution of the will?
A. Yes, as I recall, he was there.
Q. So that the three witnesses and the testator and Mr. Wolfe were present?
A. Yes.
Q. And it was in Mr. Wolfe's office?
A. Yes.
Q. Who asked you to be a witness, Mr. Sherard?
A. As I recall, Mr. Wolfe came to my office and asked me to act as a witness to the will, and I went back to this office where these other parties were present and witnessed it.
Q. Mr. Sherard, was the will read over?
A. No.
Q. In your presence?
A. No.
Q. Either before or after the execution?
A. No.
Q. Did you know who was the beneficiary?
A. No.

In re S. M. WOLFE, as Administrator, Respondent.

Q. Mr. Sherard, the will is partly typewritten and partly written in pen and ink, isn't it?
A. Yes.
Q. Have you any way of knowing of who wrote the typewritten portions thereof?
A. No, I don't.
Q. Do you know whether or not the will was prepared in Mr. Wolfe's office?
A. No, I do not.
The Court: Is it all on one sheet, Mr. Sherard?
A. Yes, sir, doubled legal. It's attached, just as the paper was manufactured.
Q. Mr. Sherard, what race was Lexius P. Henson, the testator?
A. Why, I regarded him as a mulatto. He was very light in color, almost white.
Q. Did you happen to know his wife?
A. No.
Q. Did you know any of his children?
A. No.
Q. Did he have physical defects as far as speech and hearing were concerned?
A. Well, he seemed to be a little deaf and his articulation was very bad; he stammered a little.
Q. Could you understand him without trouble in his talk?
A. Well, I think so, by paying close attention to him. I never had many words with him. I saw him very often in the building.
Q. When you went to the office for the purpose of witnessing, who did you find there?
A. Well, I couldn't say just who were present when I first went in, but at the time the will was executed Mr. Wolfe was there, Lexius P. Henson, Dr. James B. Shirley and W. J. Manos were all present when it was signed.
Q. Do you remember any conversation of any kind

that took place at the time relating to the will or to the execution thereof or to the contents?

A. Nothing was said about the contents of the will. Mr. Wolfe, I believe, asked Henson if that was his will, and he said that it was; and he requested us to sign it; and we did sign it as witnesses at his request; that is, at Henson's request.

Q. It was at Mr. Wolfe's request that Henson asked you to witness the will?

A. That is as I recall, yes.

RE-DIRECT EXAMINATION by Gen. Banham.

Q. Mr. Sherard, in your practice you have had occasion—have you or not had occasion frequently to call people in to witness papers and wills executed in your office?

A. Yes, very often.

Q. Let me ask you, Mr. Sherard, to state whether or not from your experience as a lawyer it has been customary to read over a will to the witnesses?

A. No.

DR. J. B. SHIRLEY, a witness for the Plaintiff, having duly sworn, testified as follows:

DIRECT EXAMINATION by Gen Banham.

Q. Doctor, take that paper in your hand there, please. Where do you live, doctor?

A. I live in Anderson.

Q. What is your profession?

A. Practicing Dentistry.

Q. Where is your office?

A. Peoples Bank Building.

Q. How far from where Mr. Wolfe's office used to be?

A. My office is right at the front end of the building and his was at the back, four doors between us.

Q. Look at that paper there and see if you signed it in any capacity?

A. Yes, sir, that's my signature.

Q. Who was present when you signed it, doctor?

A. There was Mr. Sherard, Mr. Manos, Mr. Wolfe, and the colored fellow Henson and myself.

Q. Were you and Mr. Sherard and Mr. Manos all present at the time that will was signed, that paper was signed by Henson?

A. Yes, sir.

Q. You saw him sign it?

A. Yes, sir.

Q. Did he see you three sign it?

A. Yes, sir.

Q. Did you see each other sign it?

A. Yes, sir, we were all there.

Q. Who requested you to sign it?

A. Mr. Wolfe came to my office and asked me to come back and sign the paper.

Q. After you got into Mr. Wolfe's office, doctor, was anything said by Henson as to his desire that you should sign it, or as to his wish that you should?

A. Yes, sir, he asked us to sign it after we were back there, said that was his will and asked us to sign the paper.

Q. Do you know Henson?

A. Slightly; he had been in my office a couple of times.

Q. In your judgment, doctor, did he have mental capacity to understand what he was doing?

A. Yes, sir, I would think so.

Q. He had, I believe, some impediment in his speech?

A. Yes, sir, a slight impediment in his speech.

Q. Could you understand him?

A. I could understand him all right.

CROSS-EXAMINATION by Mr. Hood.

Q. Mr. Shirley, was the will read over in your presence?

A. No, sir.

10

Ex Parte HUGH HESSON AND MATTIE LEE HENSON, Appellant,

Q. Did you know the contents of the will then or prior to that time?
A. No, sir.
Q. You did not know, therefore, that Mr. Wolfe was the sole beneficiary?
A. No, sir, I did not.
Q. I believe you stated that Mr. Wolfe came and asked you to go and witness the will?
A. He asked me to go back to his office and witness a paper, or something to that effect.
Q. It was witnessed in his office?
A. Yes, sir.
Q. Do you remember anything that was stated in the office by Mr. Wolfe when Henson was present?

Galley Four

A. Nothing no more than asking him if that was his will, and he said it was.
Q. Mr. Wolfe asked him if that was his will?
A. Yes, sir.
Q. And he said that it was?
A. He said it was; and we were asked to witness it for him.

W. J. MANOS, a witness for the Appellant, being duly sworn, testified as follows:
DIRECT EXAMINATION by Gen Bonham.
Q. Mr. Manos, take that paper in your hand there, please. You live in the City of Anderson, Mr. Manos?
A. Yes, sir.
Q. Were you living here in April 1918?
A. Yes, sir.
Q. Did you know Lexius Henson?
A. Yes, sir.
Q. How long had you known him, sir?
A. I had known him for three or four years.
Q. You were in the mercantile business, I believe?
A. Yes, sir.
Q. Did or not Lexius trade with you?

11

Ex Parte E. M. WOLFE, as Administrator, Respondent.

A. Yes, sir.
Q. Mr. Manos, what was his mental capacity?
A. I considered it very good.
Q. Very good?
A. Yes, sir.
Q. At the time of the execution of that paper?
A. Yes, sir.
Q. Look at it, please, sir, and see if you signed it?
A. Yes, sir.
Q. As a witness?
A. Yes, sir.
Q. Who signed it with you?
A. Jesse Sherard and Dr. Shirley.
Q. Were you all three present at the time the testator signed it?
A. Yes, sir.
Q. And when each other signed it?
A. Yes, sir.
Q. Did you or not see the testator sign it?
A. Yes, sir.
Q. And you saw each other sign it?
A. Yes, sir.
Q. Mr. Manos, where was your place of business at that time?
A. Down there on Whitner Street.
Q. On East Whitner street?
A. Yes, sir.
Q. How did you happen to go there for the purpose of—how did you happen to be there?
A. Lexius came after me.
Q. Lexius Henson?
A. Yes, sir.
Q. What did he say he wanted you for?
A. Wanted me to go down to Mr. Wolfe's office and sign a will.
Q. Did he tell you whose will it was?
A. Yes, sir.

SUPREME COURT

In re Such Henson and Mattie Lee Henson, Appellant.

Q. Where did he say it was?
A. His will.
Q. His will?
A. Yes, sir.
Q. Mr. Manos, when you got to the office, who was present?
A. Nobody but Mr. Wolfe in the office when me and him got there.
Q. Let me retrace my steps for a moment. Before you got to the office did Lexius tell you anything about the will, what was in it, or what he was going to do?
A. Before we went down to the office?
Q. Before you got to the office?
A. Yes, sir.
Q. What did he say about it?
A. He said he was going to make a temporary will until he shipped his wife.
Q. Do you know whether or not he and his wife got on amicably?
A. No, sir, they did not. That is what he told me, that him and his wife was just that way (witness crosses his fingers) all the time.
Q. At cross-purposes?
A. Yes, sir.
Q. And that he was going to ship her?
A. Yes, sir.
Q. And make a temporary will?
A. Yes, sir.
Q. Well, when you got to the office of Mr. Wolfe, what if anything passed between Mr. Wolfe and Lexius Henson about this will?
A. Well, there was a good many words passed between all of us together. It's a pretty hard master for me to remember what was said, Judge.
Q. Well, did or not Mr. Wolfe ask Henson if he understood that will, what it was for? What did he say, if anything, of that sort?

SUPREME COURT

In re S. M. WOLFE, as Administrator, Respondent.

A. Mr. Wolfe asked him if he knew what he was doing, and he said yes. He says, do you know that you are making this will debarring your wife and children from everything that you have got and making me beneficiary to it all. He says, yes.
Q. Mr. Manos, do you know Lexius Henson's handwriting?
A. No, sir.
Q. He traded with you?
A. Yes, sir.
Q. What was Lexius Henson's business, do you know?
A. Yes, sir; he was a carriage and buggy painter.
Q. Do you know who he was working with at this time, in April 1913?
A. No, I don't know who he was working with just at that time, but he worked for different men. He worked for Goss, and he worked for Johnson, that committed suicide, ever here one time, and he worked for Mr. Stephens. Them three men I know that he worked for.

CROSS-EXAMINATION by Mr. Hood.

Q. Mr. Manos, did Lexius tell you why he was going to make only a temporary will?
A. Yes, sir.
Q. What reason did he give for that?
A. That him and his wife didn't get along at all and that he was going to ship her back to where she came from, Savannah, and got rid of her and get a divorce.
Q. And, until he got her shipped and got a divorce, he was going to make a temporary will?
A. That's the way he put it up to me. It seemed like to me, the way I considered it was, that he was afraid that he might die while him and this woman that he called his wife was living together, and if he did, why then she would fall heir, and if he would

14   SUPREME COURT

Ex Parte HUGH HENSON AND MATTIE LEE HENSON, Appellant.

make a temporary will to Mr. Wolfe, why then she wouldn't get any of it; and he was aiming to ship her and get rid of her and get a divorce and marry another woman. That's what he told me he was going to do.

Q. He was pretty white, wasn't he?

A. Yes, sir, you couldn't hardly tell him from a white man.

Q. And his wife was a black woman?

A. Yes, sir.

Q. And, did he ever make any statement to you as to whether or not he was too much of a white man to be married to a black woman?

A. Yes, sir.

Q. Was that the reason that he wanted to get a divorce?

A. No, not in my opinion it wasn't.

Q. Well, of course you could only tell what he had said.

Q. Did he tell you why he wanted a divorce?

A. Yes, sir, that him and his wife wasn't getting along at all together. And he made this remark: That he wasn't no negro, nohow, and he wasn't going to live with no negro, he was going to marry him a white woman.

Q. Did he make any statement at that time about cutting out his children?

A. No, sir, he didn't mention his children to me.

Q. Did Mr. Wolfe, at any time while you were in the office with Lex for the purpose of witnessing the will, tell Henson, Lexius Henson, that he could make a will cutting out his wife and still leave the property to his children?

A. No, he didn't tell him that.

Q. How many children did Lex have, or did you know?

A. I don't remember seeing but two, a little boy and a little girl.

Q. You were present at the trial of this case in the Probate Court, were you not, Mr. Manos?

SUPREME COURT   15

In Re S. M. WOLFE, as Administrator, Respondent.

A. Yes, sir.

Q. Do you remember a letter that was then introduced in evidence by Mr. Wolfe, written by Lexius Henson?

A. Yes, sir.

Gen Bonham: We object, may it please the Court; the letter is the best evidence.

Q. Do you remember the contents of that letter, Mr. Manos?

A. Yes, sir.

Gen Bonham: We object, may it please the Court.

The Court: What do you answer? You can answer that yes or no.

A. No, sir, I don't remember the contents.

Q. Do you remember that in that letter he—

Gen. Bonham: I object, may it please the Court, to Mr. Hood's stating the contents of that letter here in the presence of the jury, when the letter is the best evidence.

The Court: This witness has already answered, Mr. Hood, that he doesn't remember the contents of the letter.

Mr. Hood: Yes, but he might remember, Your Honor, please, is given statement or an independent fact in that letter.

The Court: If they object to it I will have to rule against it, unless you can show that the letter has been destroyed, then you can later put him, or as you please, as you see fit. But if the letter can be had the letter is the best evidence, and the law requires the best evidence so long as you can get it. When you can't get the best evidence, take the next best.

Q. Mr. Manos, was the will read over in your presence?

A. Yes, sir, as well as I can remember it was read over in my presence.

Q. Who read it?

A. Mr. Wolfe. He either read it all or a portion

of it, but he did read the will in my presence. And I wasn't interested in it, I couldn't swear whether he read it all or not, but he did read a part of the will, anyway, probably all of it; I don't know now.

Q. And he told Lex what with regard to what would happen if he signed it?

A. Told Lex, do you know that you are depriving your wife and children of all you have got and if you die I will get all that you have got under this will, or something to that effect.

Q. And what did Lex reply?

A. That's all right, that's all right.

Q. Did he say that's all right, that it's only a temporary will?

A. No, sir, he didn't tell Mr. Wolfe anything about it being a temporary will, he told me that.

Q. He told you that before he got there?

A. Yes, sir, he told me that going up there.

Q. Mr. Bemros, what became of the will after it was executed?

A. Well, me and Lex left there and left the will in the office. We left the will with Mr. Wolfe.

Q. Do you know what became of it.

A. No, sir; I suppose Mr. Wolfe takes charge of it.

Q. Mr. Bemros, you stated that you were in the grocery business. Was Lexius a customer of yours?

A. Yes, sir.

Q. Did he provide for his wife and children?

A. I think he did, all right.

Q. How often did he come to your place of business for the purpose of buying groceries?

A. Well, he made Saturday his regular day, he was there every Saturday, and he come sometimes through the week, but he was there every Saturday morning about the first man.

Q. How long did he keep that up, Mr. Bemros?

A. As long as he traded with me. I don't know

how long he traded with me, but he traded with me I think about three or four years.

Q. Mr. Bemros, do you know when his wife died?

A. No, sir, I do not.

Q. Do you know when she left Anderson?

A. No, sir, I do not.

Q. Mr. Bemros, you testified a little while ago that as you recalled now Mr. Wolfe read the will or a part of it to Lex at the time you went up there for the purpose of witnessing it?

A. That's my best recollection about it, Judge.

Q. You testified, of course, in the Probate Court on this matter?

A. Yes, sir.

Q. Let me read this then and ask you, Mr. Bemros, whether you remember to have testified thus, commencing with the question, "(Q) Was the will read over in your presence? (A) No, sir. I declare, I don't remember. I think, to the best of my recollection, Mr. Wolfe was preparing the will or did finish preparing the will after I got up there. I was up there for a little bit, me and Lex, before the will was signed and there was a right smart little talk between Mr. Wolfe and Lex and myself while we was up there, but I don't remember whether he read the will over or not."

A. Yes, sir.

Q. Is that probably correct?

A. I remember that very distinctly. But since then—it was three or four years, you know before that testimony, and I had never had my mind refreshed upon it, and since that time I have thought quite a lot about it and my recollection has been refreshed on it and I am satisfied that he did read over a part of the will or all of it to me. Because he drew the will, I saw him drawing the will.

Q. You saw who drawing the will?

A. Mr. Wolfe.

SUPREME COURT 18

Ex Parte HUGH BENSON AND MATTIE LEE BENSON, Appellant.

Q. You saw Mr. Wolfe drawing the will?
A. Yes, sir, on the typewriter.
Q. And he read, you think, the will or a part of it over to you at the time?
A. Yes, sir, I feel like I am safe now in saying that he did read part of it, if not all of it, to me.
Q. And you saw Mr. Wolfe preparing the will that he read over to you on the typewriter?
A. Yes, sir.
Q. Now the will that you witnessed there is not written in typewriting, is it, Mr. Manos?
A. Well, it looks like there is some of it in type-writing.
Q. Look at the will and see whether it's in typewriting or not?
A. No, that ain't. I can just say that I saw him writing on the typewriter. He was writing something on the typewriter, and he said it was the will; that's all I know.
Q. What he read you was what he was writing on the typewriter?
A. Yes, sir, I reckon so. I didn't make my close investigation.
Q. You don't know then that he read that will that you witnessed in your presence or any part of that will?
A. No, sir, I couldn't swear that that's what he read to me.
Q. Mr. Manos, you knew Lexius very well?
A. Yes, sir, I reckon I did.
Q. And you were not only his groceryman but you were rather his advisor in his little affairs, were you not?
A. Yes, sir, he came to me a good many times for advice.
Q. And who was his attorney?
A. Mr. Wolfe.

SUPREME COURT 19

In Re S. M. WOLFE, as Administrator, Respondent.

Q. How did you know that Mr. Wolfe was his attorney?
A. He told me so.
Q. Who?
A. Lex told me that.
Q. Did you know of any special attachment between them, or any reason for it, Mr. Manos?
A. No, sir, I didn't know of any reason for it, only he just like everybody else, I reckon, just had his preference.

RE-DIRECT EXAMINATION by Gen. Bonham.

Q. Do you or not know whether Lex did have a very sincere attachment for Mr. Wolfe?
A. I didn't quite catch that, Judge.
Q. I said, do you or not know that Lex did have an attachment for Mr. Wolfe?
A. An attachment for him?
Q. Yes—affection for him?
A. He was very favorable of him, always spoke that way, as an attorney.
Q. Mr. Manos, that paper was signed in 1918, April 1918. Does it come within your knowledge that Lexius Hemton's wife died shortly after that?
A. Well, sir, I don't know when she died. The first I heard of her dying is when this case come up. I didn't know that she was dead until this case come up.
Q. Do you know when Lex died?
A. No, sir, I don't know when he died either.

RE-CROSS-EXAMINATION by Mr. Hood.

Q. Did you have any conversation with Mr. Wolfe with regard to this matter after the will was developed, after the will was probated, I mean, after the death of Lexius Hemson?
A. Well, I don't know whether you would call it a conversation or not; he met me on the street out there one day and brought me into the Probate's office and showed me the will and asked me if I remembered signing the will, and I told him I did.

SUPREME COURT

Ex Parte HUGH HENSON AND HATTIE LEE HENSON, Appellant.

Q. What else was said, Mr. Mamos, if anything?

A. I bo-dog if I remember, Judge. It's a pretty hard matter for me to remember all the little things.

Q. Did he tell you why he hadn't presented the will earlier?

A. Oh, well, I believe he said that he didn't know Lex was dead, and he had wrote to Mr. Goss a time or two and Mr. Goss had failed, or forgotten, to answer his letter, and he didn't know that he was dead until he come down here and somebody told him, I believe he said he went to see Mr. Goss and asked him why do didn't answer his letters, and Mr. Goss says, why, he is dead. Then he says, I believe, as well as I can remember, well, I have got some papers in my safe, I think; and he went and found that he had a will. I think me and Mr. Wolfe had a conversation something similar to that; that was about the sum and substance of it.

Q. And he didn't know that Lex was dead until on that occasion, and on finding out that he was dead, he went to his safe and got the will and brought it and probated it?

A. As well as I remember he didn't know he was dead until Mr. Goss told him. That was my recollection, that he didn't know it until Mr. Goss informed him, and then he went to his safe and found these papers in the safe. That's my recollection.

Q. Well, do you remember any other conversation, then er at any other time, with Mr. Wolfe in regard to the matter, Mr. Mamos?

A. I can't recall just at the present time. I can't refresh my memory on any other conversation just at this minute.

Mr. Dagnall: We offer the will in evidence. Your Honor.

Ex Parte H. M. WOLFE vs. Administrator, Respondent.

will introduced in evidence and marked exhibit A.

State of South Carolina, } Last Will and Testament
Anderson County   } Lexius P. Henson

I, Lexius P. Henson, at present of City of Anderson, in the County and State above named, being of sound and disposing mind, and of ordinary bodily health, and absolutely without inducement, or any suggestion or influence on the part of the beneficiary herein, do now make and declare this to be my last, solemn will and testament to wit: that in the event of my dying a grass widower, a widower, or married to my present wife Hattie Henson, I will and bequeath to my friend and attorney Samuel M. Wolfe my entire estate consisting of Life Insurance under the policy in the Metropolitan Life Insurance Co. and under the policy in the Life and Casualty Insurance Company of Tennessee, and all other personalty or realty whatsoever, for his sole and absolute property, my wife and children being without affection for me and my wife being undutiful, perverse and a source of constant annoyance and disturbance, and there being no one else except a brother whose whereabouts I do not know and my lawyer aforesaid being my preference and the one I feel most attachment for.

Witness my hand and seal this 30th day of April, A. D. 1918.

Lexius P. Henson. (Seal)

The foregoing instrument was subscribed, sealed, published and declared by Lexius P. Henson as and for his last will and testament in our presence and in the presence of each of us, and we, at his request, at the same time, in his presence, and in the presence of each of us, hereunto subscribed our names as attesting witnesses thereto, and to the fact that in our opin-

CRAIG E. RUSH

SUPREME COURT 22

Ex Parte RUSH HENSON and MATTIE LEE HENSON, Appellant.

tor, testator is of apparent sound and disposing mind.

This 30th April, 1918.

J. L. Sherard.
W. J. Mancss.
Jas. R. Shirley.

P. S. LEWIS, a witness for the appellant, being duly sworn, testified as follows:

DIRECT EXAMINATION by Mr. Dagnall.

Q. Mr. Lewis, where do you live?

A. Here in Anderson.

Q. What position do you hold with the Life & Casualty Insurance Company of Tennessee?

A. Soliciting and collecting insurance.

Q. Have you ever seen this policy before, Mr. Lewis? (presenting same). Are you familiar with that policy?

A. Yes, sir.

Q. Tell how what Lexius Henson did in reference to that policy about having it changed?

Mr. Paget: Do you know of your own knowledge? Did you have anything to do with it, Mr. Lewis?

A. Well, it was changed. He brought it to the office to be changed in October. It has been changed twice there at his request.

Q. What was his request?

A. To make it to his estate the last time.

Q. Now when was the last time he had it changed?

A. The last time this was changed was May 13, 1918, and made to his estate.

Mr. Dagnall: We offer this policy in evidence.

Mr. Paget: We can't see where there is any competency in that policy, and we object to it on the ground that it's irrelevant.

The Court: I will let it go in for what it's worth. So far as the body of the policy is concerned it has nothing to do with this, except that it might have some bearing on the point of whether or not the man had

SUPREME COURT 23

Ex R. S. M. WOLFE, an Administrator, Respondent.

sense enough to attend to his own business.

Policy introduced in evidence and marked exhibit R.

Q. Who requested that assignment?

A. Lexius.

CROSS-EXAMINATION by Mr. Head.

Q. Mr. Lewis, did his wife ever give permission or consent to the transfer of the assignment?

A. No, sir.

Q. What is the amount of that policy?

A. I don't remember. I never indeed it.

A. Won't you look at it, please, sir?

A. Fifty dollars is all.

Q. Is that on Lexius Henson in favor of his wife?

A. That's the original beneficiary, yes, sir, his wife. You see, it was changed at his request. On May 12, 1918, he had it changed to his estate.

Q. Didn't have it changed to Mr. Wolfe?

A. No, sir.

Q. What was the date of it?

A. The date of the policy?

Q. No, sir, the date of that transfer?

A. On May 13, 1918.

Q. Yes, sir.

A. The will, I believe, was executed April 20, 1918.

No other questions.

H. D. GOSS, a witness for the appellant, being duly sworn, testified as follows:

DIRECT EXAMINATION by Mr. Dagnall.

Q. Mr. Goss, where do you live?

A. Anderson.

Q. How long have you lived here, Mr. Goss.

A. About fourteen years, sir.

Q. Mr. Goss, did you know Lexius P. Henson?

A. Yes, sir.

Ex Parte HENRY HENSON AND MATTIE LEE HENSON, Appellant.

Q. How long did you know him?
A. About six or seven years.
Q. What was his occupation?
A. Carriage painter.
Q. Mr. Goss, what was Lexius Henson's mental condition?
A. I would judge him to be a pretty keen sort of fellow, sir.
Q. Do you know anything about his domestic relations?
A. I had heard him say several times that he didn't get along well with his wife.
Q. Well, what did he say about it, do you remember?
A. Nothing in particular, sir, only he had some trouble with her.
Q. Did he ever make any statement to you about his wife and children, about their attitude towards him?
A. Yes, sir, I believe he did.
Q. What did he say about the attitude of his wife and children towards him?
A. Well, they didn't get along very well, and they didn't provide, something about the cooking, or something or other. He said they failed to cook for him.
Q. Mr. Goss, did he work for you?
A. Yes, sir.
Q. How long did he work for you?
A. I expect about four years to the best of my knowledge, three or four years.
Q. Did you receive a letter from Mr. Wolfe or not?
A. Yes, sir.
Q. About Henson?
A. Yes, sir.
Q. Did you answer that?
A. No, sir.

In re S. M. WOLFE, et Administrator, Respondent

Q. When did you first inform Mr. Wolfe of the death of Henson?
A. When he asked me, sir.
Q. That was in Anderson here?
A. Yes, sir.
Q. What was the mental capacity of Henson, could you say?
A. Good, yes, sir, I would think.
Q. Do you know what Henson thought of Mr. Wolfe? Did he ever talk to you about Mr. Wolfe?
A. Very often.
Q. What did he say about Mr. Wolfe?
A. He never would do anything without he consulted Mr. Wolfe.
Q. Did he ever tell you what his personal feelings for Mr. Wolfe were?
A. Very, very friendly, sir.
Q. Do you know whether or not Mr. Wolfe knew of Henson's death before you told him?
A. That I can't say, sir; I think not.
Q. How long after Henson's death before you told Mr. Wolfe?
A. I couldn't say, sir, as to that, I don't remember; I know it was some time after I failed to answer the letter.
Q. Do you know when Henson went to Augusta?
A. The date I can't say, sir.
Q. How long was he in Augusta before he died?
A. That I can't say, sir.

CROSS-EXAMINATION by Mr. Hood.

Q. Mr. Goss, you said that the relations between Mr. Wolfe and Lex was very friendly?
A. I should judge so, yes, sir.
Q. And the relations between you and Lex were friendly also, weren't they, and the relations between him and Mr. Manos over there were very friendly, too, weren't they?

26

SUPREME COURT

A. Well, I understood so.

Q. Did Lex ever threaten to make a will in your favor because he was very friendly to you and that his wife failed to cook for him?

A. Well, that I can't say, sir.

Q. Oh, yes, you can; you know whether he ever told you that or not. You never heard of him making a will to Mr. Manos, toward whom he was very friend-ly, because his wife wouldn't cook for him have you?

A. No, sir.

Q. And why was it, Mr. Goss, that Mr. Wolfe had apparently to depend on you to let him know whether his friend who had made him sole beneficiary was liv-ing or dead? Couldn't Mr. Wolfe keep up with him as well as you?

A. I suppose on account that he thought he was working for me; that's all I know.

Q. When Lex left here did you correspond with Lex?

A. No, sir.

Q. Did you have any special interest in keeping up with Lex's whereabouts after he left Anderson?

A. Not any more than I expected him to come back soon.

Q. And if Mr. Wolfe had wanted to keep up with him he could have conducted a correspondence with him, could he not?

A. I couldn't say as to that, sir.

RE-DIRECT EXAMINATION by Mr. Dagnall.

Q. Mr. Goss, state whether or not Lexdus Henson ever slept in your shop?

A. Yes, sir.

Q. Do you know how often?

Mr. Hood: Your Honor, please, I object to that. I don't think it's relevant. He could have slept at other places.

The Court: Well, that may have some probative

27

SUPREME COURT

value to show whether or not he stayed at home and whether or not this man knew him well, this witness.

Q. How often did he sleep in the shop?

A. That I can't say, but he slept there very often. occasionally.

Q. Mr. Goss, tell what Henson did with his brushes when he went to Augusta?

A. He left them in the shop.

Q. How long was he gone now before you heard of his death?

A. Judge, that's pretty hard for me, I don't remem-ber.

Q. Just give us some idea—thirty, sixty or ninety days?

A. In the neighborhood I suppose of thirty days; possibly longer.

Q. How old was Lex in your opinion?

A. I couldn't say, sir.

Q. You can't give us any estimate?

A. No, sir, I haven't much of an idea how old he was.

RE-CROSS-EXAMINATION by Mr. Hood.

Q. Mr. Goss, Lex got drunk sometimes, didn't he?

A. Well, I believe he did, sir.

Q. And he would likely when he was drunk sleep in the shop?

A. Well, I couldn't hardly say as to that.

Q. When he left your place and went to Augusta he left worn out brushes and an old worthless pair of overalls at your shop, did you not testify in the former trial, and that was all he did leave there, wasn't it?

A. Brushes and some overalls, yes, sir.

Q. They were discarded, worthless?

A. They were brushes that had been used, yes, sir.

EXAMINATION by Mr. Dagnall.

Q. Those brushes were still good then, were they?

A. Well, Judge, they were good, yes, sir, but Mr.

SUPREME COURT 23

Hugh Paul Hizzon and Mattie Lee Henson, Appellant.

Hood asked me if they had been used—yes, sir.

PAUL S. STEVENS, a witness for the appellant, being duly sworn, testified as follows:

DIRECT EXAMINATION by Mr. Dagnall.

Q. Mr. Stevens, where do you live?

A. I live in Anderson.

Q. How long have you been living here?

A. Forty-nine years.

Q. What is your business, Mr. Stevens?

A. Farming.

Q. And also proprietor of this shop for years on South Main?

A. No, sir, I have sold that business.

Q. You were proprietor of a shop down here on South Main for a good many years?

A. Yes, sir.

Q. Mr. Stevens, did you know Lexius Henson?

A. Yes, sir, I knew him.

Q. How long did you know him?

A. Well, I suppose, sir, about twenty years.

Q. Did he ever do any work for you?

A. He worked for my father a long time. He worked for us, just off and on, probably some six or seven years, just occasionally.

Q. Mr. Stevens, you knew him pretty well?

A. Yes, sir, I knew him pretty well.

Q. Well, now, what was his mental condition?

A. Well, it was all right. He was just a little cranky, but he had plenty of sense.

Q. In your opinion he knew how he wanted his property to go? He had sense enough to know what he wanted to do with his property?

A. Yes, sir, I think so, sir.

Q. Well, what was his mental condition as compared with the average negro?

A. Well, he was brighter than the average darkey.

Q. You think he was above the average?

SUPREME COURT 29

To Mr. S. M. WOLFE, as Administrator, Respondent

A. Yes, sir.

CROSS-EXAMINATION by Mr. Hood.

Q. Mr. Stevens, you, of course, weren't present at the execution of the will?

A. I beg your pardon?

Q. You weren't present at the time he signed that paper purporting to be a will?

A. No, sir.

Q. You don't know what his mental condition at that time was?

A. No, sir.

Q. Mr. Stevens, you said you knew him for about twenty years and you looked on him as being above the average. How did he take care of his family, as far as you know?

A. I don't know, sir; he never did mention them to me.

Q. Did you ever hear of his failing to support his wife and children?

A. No, sir, never did.

Q. Did you ever hear of him living separate and apart from them?

A. No, sir.

Q. As far as you know, he lived with them and supported them throughout?

A. So far as I know, yes, sir.

RE-DIRECT EXAMINATION by Mr. Dagnall.

Q. Mr. Stevens, how old a man was Henson?

A. Well, I don't know, sir; he was older than I, a right smart.

Q. Well, I hate to ask you how old you are?

A. Well, I expect he was about seventy years old.

S. W. WILLIFORD, a witness for the appellant, being duly sworn, testified as follows:

DIRECT EXAMINATION by Mr. Dagnall.

Q. Mr. Williford, where do you live?

A. I live in Anderson.

SUPREME COURT

In re HUGH HERNDON AND MATTIE LEE HERNDON, Appellant.

Q. How long have you lived here?
A. I have been in the City about twenty-one or two years; I was born and raised in the County.
Q. County bred, then?
A. Yes, sir, County bred.
Q. Mr. Williford, did you know Lexius Henson?
A. Yes, sir.
Q. How long did you know him?
A. Why, some ten or twelve years; I don't know hardly how long; something like eight or ten years.
Q. Did you ever have any business dealings with him?
A. Yes, sir, he traded with me a long time, traded a grocery bill.
Q. What was Lexius Henson's mental condition?
A. Why, I would take him to be about like the average man.
Q. How did you think he was at the time of his death?
A. I declare, I have no idea. He was up in sixty, I would say, just guessing at it. I never did ask him his age.
Q. Comparing Henson with the negro race, what would you say about his being below or above the average?
A. He was a little above the average negro.
Q. So you found him in your business dealings with him pretty keen?
A. Yes, sir, he had plenty of sense. Of course, he was a little bit queer, and he couldn't hear good, and he had bad talk in his language.
Q. Have you ever heard him say anything about Mr. Wolfe?
A. No sir. The only thing he said was that Mr. Wolfe was his attorney.
Q. I reckon he was rather proud of that fact?
A. That's the only thing I ever heard him say, that Mr. Wolfe was his attorney.

SUPREME COURT

In re E. M. WOLFE, et. Administrator, Respondent.

CROSS-EXAMINATION by Mr. Hood.
Q. Mr. Williford, you are engaged in the mercantile business?
A. Yes, sir.
Q. And Lexius was a patron of yours, as he was of Mr. Manes?
A. Yes, sir.
Q. Paying stuff for his wife and children?
A. I suppose so, that's where it always went.
Q. Did you ever hear of his not providing for his wife and children?
A. No, sir.
Q. Both as to food and clothing and a house to live in?
A. I never heard of any complaint any way.
Q. You say you know him some ten or twelve years?
A. Yes, sir, at least ten or twelve years.
Q. You never heard him make any special statement with regard to his relation toward Mr. Wolfe?
A. No, sir; the only thing, he just said Mr. Wolfe was his attorney.
Q. Did you know Lexius' children?
A. Yes, sir, I knew them when I seen them there in the store.
Q. Would you know them now if you were to see them?
A. Yes, sir, I would know them, but they have outgrowed themselves since they left there.
Q. Mr. Williford, will you look at these children and tell whether you recognize them as being Lexius Henson's children?
A. Yes, sir, that's his boy and girl. I know the boy better than I do the girl.
Q. But you recognize them as being his children?
A. Yes, sir, that's the same ones that always come

in the store, and he said they were his children. They have come in there for years, ever since they was little children.

G. H. GEIGER, a witness for appellant, being duly sworn, testified as follows:

DIRECT EXAMINATION by Mr. Dagnall.

Q. Mr. Geiger, where do you live?
A. I live in the City of Anderson.
Q. What is your business?
A. I am a lawyer.
Q. You are a magistrate, too?
A. Yes, sir.
Q. How long have you been magistrate?
A. Something over eight years.
Q. Mr. Geiger, examine that will. Is that writing there the handwriting of Mr. Wolfe?
A. No, that's not Mr. Wolfe's handwriting.
Q. You are familiar with Mr. Wolfe's handwriting?
A. Yes, sir.
Q. Did you know Lexius Henson?
A. Yes, sir, I knew him.
Q. What was his mental capacity?
A. It was good.
Q. Did you see him about the time of the execution of the will?
A. I think so; he was in and out the office a good ceal along about that time.
Q. What would you estimate his age to have been?
A. That would be right hard to say. I would think he was fifty or sixty years old. A man though could be older than his appearance might indicate, or younger.
Q. Comparing Henson with others of the negro race, was he above or below the average in intelligence?
A. Why, I would consider him above the average in intelligence.

CROSS-EXAMINATION by Mr. Hood.

Q. Mr. Geiger, your office at that time, and is now, as far as that's concerned, upstairs over the Peoples Bank?
A. Yes, sir.
Q. And yours and Mr. Sherard's and Mr. Wolfe's offices were all there in a row, were they not?
A. Yes, sir, Mr. Wolfe had the end office, and I had two offices and then Mr. Sherard's came next.
Q. Mr. Geiger, did Mr. Wolfe ever discuss this will or the making of it with you prior to the making and execution of it?
A. No, sir, I didn't know nothing about it until it was probated.
Q. You knew nothing about it or nothing of the contents of it?
A. No, sir.

S. W. WILLIFORD, a witness for appellant, recalled, testified as follows:

RE-DIRECT EXAMINATION by Mr. Dagnall.

Q. Mr. Williford, are you familiar with the hand-writing of Henson?
A. Just tolerable; of course I can't be positive on it.
Q. Look at this handwriting there and tell the Court and jury whether in your opinion that's Henson's handwriting?
A. It looks like his handwriting. Of course, I can't be positive about that part of it, but the signature looks more like it. You see, I received orders from him, and you never pay much attention to that part as you will to a man's signature; you will soon learn it. That sort of looks like his writing. I won't be positive about it.

RE-CROSS-EXAMINATION by Mr. Williford, that he was capable of the construction of the will, as well as writing it? For instance, would he be capable of preparing this as will without assistance? You heard it read over, did you not?

A. Yes, sir. I don't know whether he would or not, now. That's mighty hard to answer.

Q. "I, Lexius P. Henson, at present of the City of Anderson, State above named...." That sounds like legal style, don't it?

A. Yes, sir.

Q. "being of sound and disposing mind and of ordinary bodily health, and absolutely without inducement or any suggestion of influence on the part of the beneficiary herein...." Do you reckon Lexius could have made that?

A. No, sir.

Gen. Bonham: I object to that. Counsel is standing up there making an argument to the jury under the pretense of examining the witness.

The Court: I will let him answer the question.

Q. "or any suggestion of influence on the part of the beneficiary herein, do now make and declare this to be my last solemn will and testament, to-wit: that in the event of my dying a grass widower, a widower or married to my present wife, Hattie Henson, I will and bequeath to my friend and attorney, Samuel M. Wolfe....." Do you think he was capable of having constructed that, Mr. Williford?

Gen. Bonham: I object to it; it may it please the Court. That is the very question that jury has got to answer, not this witness.

The Court: I really don't think it makes a particle of difference, Mr. Hood, the point in the case is whether or not Lexius knew what he was doing at the time he signed that will and what that will contained. Not whether he would have the ability to draft a will of that kind, but did he know that that will was giving the whole of his property to Mr. Wolfe. It he had

sense enough to know that, that's all that was necessary.

Mr. Hood: May Your Honor, please, that's the very thing that is involved here—would he have sense enough to write and understand that will. Now in response to their question, Mr. Williford says that it looks like Lexius' handwriting, that in his opinion he probably wrote it. Now the question is, whether from his knowledge of Lexius, Lexius would have ability to compose and understand, or to understand, whether he composed or not, the meaning of those words and the meaning of that will as a whole.

The Court: Well, now, that's a different proposition.

Gen. Bonham: Our objection is just this: that counsel is endeavoring to substitute the opinion of this witness, the answer of this witness for the answers that that jury has got to make from all the evidence that is induced in this case.

The Court: I would like for this witness to say again as to what knowledge he had of this man. Did you know him very well—Lexius?

A. Yes, sir. I knew him for years, several years.

The Court: How many years?

A. Why, something like I suppose between ten and twelve, something like that; I won't be positive; a long time.

The Court: And had business transactions with him?

A. Yes, sir, he traded his grocery bill) with me every week. He traded his market bill with Manos. He commenced when he first come here with Johnson down there; that was about his first work; he commenced trading with me, and he traded as long as he stayed here.

The Court: Then you had opportunities to size him up as to his mental capacity?

A. Why, he was all right. Henson was a little

gister, he couldn't talk good, and his hearing was bad. Of course, you know, that would make him look a little off.

The Court: Gentlemen, I doubt whether I should take that question out of that statement; and it's on cross-examination also. As I understand, this is your witness?

Gen. Bonham: Yes, sir.

The Court: Well, I think I had better let him answer the question.

Q. Mr. Williford, the question was, then, whether you thought that Lexius could have, or did, compose that will?

A. I couldn't tell you that.

The Court: I understood the question to be as to whether or not he thought he had the ability to compose a will of that sort.

A. Well, Mr. Williford, in your opinion did Lexius have the mental capacity or the ability to have composed that will as I read it to you a little ago?

A. I couldn't hardly say. I tell you, it would take a pretty well educated man and a right smart of brains to word it out like it is here. I don't know, I don't want to be the judge on that.

EXAMINATION IN REPLY by Mr. Dagnall.

Q. Mr. Williford, Lexius Henson, though, if he had copied that, had ability to know that Mr. Wolfe would be getting everything and his wife and children getting nothing, wouldn't he?

A. Yes, sir, he could have copied it very easily.

Q. And would have known that Mr. Wolfe was getting it all under that?

A. Yes, sir, he had that much sense, I know.

RE-CROSS-EXAMINATION by Mr. Paget.

Q. I believe you said you knew Lexius Henson's handwriting?

A. Of course, I never said positive it was his.

Q. You won't say positive that was his writing?

A. No, sir.

Q. Look at that and see if you think this is?

A. No, sir, I couldn't tell you. If I could see his signature, you see—

Q. How about that?

A. Yes, sir, that looks like his signature.

Q. Would you say that he wrote that?

A. I can't say; it looks sort of like his writing. I never noticed his writing as much as his orders. As a rule you will notice a man's signature.

Q. You would be as positive as to that as you would to this?

A. Yes, sir, it looks like it. Of course, it's been so long I get it mixed up.

Paper marked C. V. S. for identification.

R. E. WILSON, a witness for appellant, being duly sworn, testified as follows:

DIRECT EXAMINATION by Mr. Dagnall.

Q. Mr. Wilson, where do you live?

A. I live in Anderson.

Q. What is your business?

A. I'm a lawyer, sir.

Q. How long have you been living here, Mr. Wilson?

A. Since January 1st, 1919.

Q. Mr. Wilson, did you know Lexius Henson?

A. Yes, sir, I knew him.

Q. Did you ever have any business transactions with him?

A. Yes, sir, I had some business transactions with him in the Spring of 1919, as I recall, or the Summer of 1919.

Q. Where was your office?

A. Why, I was then in the office of Mr. Wolfe; that is, it was Mr. Wolfe's office prior to the time I came here; I rented it from him.

In re HUGH HENSON AND NAFIE LEE BENSON, Appellant.

queer; he couldn't talk good, and his hearing was bad. Of course, you know, that would make him look a little queer.

The Court: Gentlemen, I doubt whether I should take that question out of that statement; and it's on cross-examination also. As I understand, this is your witness?

Geo. Benham: Yes, sir.

The Court: Well, I think I had better let him answer the question.

Q. Mr. Williford, the question was, then, whether you thought that Lexius could have, or did, compose that will?

A. I couldn't tell you that.

The Court: I understood the question to be as to whether or not he thought he had the ability to compose a will of that sort.

Q. Well, Mr. Williford, in your opinion did Lexius have the mental capacity or the ability to have composed that will as I read it to you a little ago?

A. I couldn't hardly say. I tell you, it would take a pretty well educated man and a right smart of brains to word it out like it is here. I don't know. I don't want to be the judge on that.

EXAMINATION IN REPLY by Mr. Dagnall.

Q. Mr. Williford, Lexius Henson, though, if he had copied that, had ability to know that Mr. Wolfe would be getting everything and his wife and children getting nothing, wouldn't he?

A. Yes, sir, he could have copied it very easily.

Q. And would have known that Mr. Wolfe was getting it all under that?

A. Yes, sir, he had that much sense, I know.

RE-CROSS-EXAMINATION by Mr. Paget.

Q. I believe you said you knew Lexius Henson's handwriting?

A. Of course, I never said positive it was his.

In re M. WOLFE, as Administrator, Respondent.

Q. You won't say positive that was his writing?

A. No, sir.

Q. Look at that and see if you think this is?

A. No, sir. I couldn't tell you. If I could see his signature, you see—

Q. How about that?

A. Yes, sir, that looks like his signature.

Q. Would you say that he wrote that?

A. I can't say; it looks sort of like his writing. I never noticed his writing as much as his orders. As a rule you will notice a man's signature.

Q. You would be as positive as to that as you would to this?

A. Yes, sir, it looks like it. Of course, it's been so long I get it mixed up.

Paper marked C. V. S. for identification.

R. E. WILSON, a witness for appellant, being duly sworn, testified as follows:

DIRECT EXAMINATION by Mr. Dagnall.

Q. Mr. Wilson, where do you live?

A. I live in Anderson.

Q. What is your business?

A. I'm a lawyer, sir.

Q. How long have you been living here, Mr. Wilson?

A. Since January 1st, 1919.

Q. Mr. Wilson, did you know Lexius Henson?

A. Yes, sir, I knew him.

Q. Did you ever have any business transactions with him?

A. Yes, sir, I had some business transactions with him in the Spring of 1919, as I recall, or the Summer of 1919.

Q. Where was your office?

A. Why, I was then in the office of Mr. Wolfe; that is, it was Mr. Wolfe's office prior to the time I came here; I rented it from him.

Q. And when Mr. Wolfe went to Columbia?
A. I rented his office from him, yes, sir.
Q. Now you say Lexius Henson came to see you?
A. Yes, sir.
Q. What did he want?
A. He wanted me, as attorney, to eject some ten-
ants from a house that belonged to him, or that he had
rented or subrented, I forget which.
Q. Well, what did you tell him?
A. Why, we had some considerable discussion
about it. He came to see me right frequently for a
week or two and wanted me to do this work for him,
this legal work. I asked him for a fee of twenty dollars, I think, and he wanted me to credit him for the
fee. I had never seen him before—

Mr. Hood: Your Honor, please, we don't know
what our friend is leading up to, but it seems to me to
be wholly irrelevant.

Mr. Dagnall: This shows mental condition also, a
man wanting to get credit.

Q. Well, what did he tell you about Mr. Wolfe?
Mr. Hood: Your Honor, please, I object. That's a
statement purporting to be made by a man that is now
dead, and it's hearsay testimony.

The Court: Well, if it tends to show how he felt
towards Mr. Wolfe, why I think it would be competent.

A. After some discussion about the fee, Mr. Dagnall, I refused to give him credit, and he insisted on
credit. He referred me to Mr. Wolfe, and at that time
said that he had made Mr. Wolfe his heir, and seemed
to think for that reason I would extend him credit.
Q. How long was that after Mr. Wolfe left Anderson, Mr. Wilson?
A. Why, Mr. Dagnall, I don't recall exactly, I think
it was some six or eight months; possibly not so long,
and possibly longer.

Q. So he stated that he had made Mr. Wolfe his
heir?
A. He did, yes, sir.
Q. Do you remember what time of the year it was?
A. Why, I think it was in the late Spring or Sum-
mer of 1919.
Mr. Hood: No questions.

S. M. WOLFE, appellant, being duly sworn, testified
as follows:

DIRECT EXAMINATION by Mr. Dagnall.
Q. Mr. Wolfe, where do you live?
A. Well, I am officially residing in Columbia.
Q. Where did you live before you moved to Co-
lumbia?
A. Anderson.
Q. What official position do you hold by the State
government?
A. I am now occupying the position as Attorney
General of the State.
Q. Mr. Wolfe, did you know Lexius Henson?
A. Yes, sir.
Q. How long did you know him?
A. When I was practicing law here I knew Lexius
in a way. He consulted me on various occasions, I
represented him three or four times in some matters,
and I had occasion to know him, I suppose, Mr. Dagnall, covering a period of about four or five years.
Q. Now, Mr. Wolfe, tell your connection with that
will that's been introduced in evidence.
A. Lexius consulted me on various occasions—
Mr. Hood: May Your Honor please, I am going to
object to that, because that's a very broad question
to tell what his connection is with that will, and I take
it that that means to involve the question of what
transpired between him and Henson. We therefore
object to the testimony under the Section of the Code
which prohibits one who is seeking an advantage at

the hands of a dead man to testify as to any words or transactions.

Mr. Dagrall: Of course, I only meant for the witness to testify to the competent evidence. I will get to the concrete question directly.

The Court: All right. That's the hardest Section I know of to apply in a case.

Q. Mr. Wolfe, is that in your handwriting, that will?

A. That will is not in my handwriting.

Q. How much of it did you prepare?

A. I prepared the attestation clause, which is the typewritten portion at the conclusion of the will.

Q. How about the top?

Mr. Hood: May Your Honor please, that's going directly, it seems to me, into a transaction with the deceased. He is going right into the matter of the preparation of that will, saying that he did the typewritten portion of it, and if that isn't going into a transaction with the deceased I don't know what would be.

The Court: I think he can answer that.

Mr. Faget excepts.

The Court: He can answer as to whether or not that's his handwriting.

Q. Is this your handwriting?

A. It is not.

Q. Did you write the typewritten part, the bottom, the attestation clause?

A. I did.

Q. Did you write any other part of it?

A. I did not.

Q. Who wrote it?

A. Lex just wrote that himself. And if there is no objection, Your Honor, I would like to explain it.

Q. I am going to ask you to explain your connection—

A. I will.

SUPREME COURT   41

In re H. H. WOLFE, as Administrator. Respondent.

The Court: I think he can answer that question that he has answered already, that he didn't write it, or what portion he did write, and that Lexius wrote it. I don't think that would be a transaction between them, if he knows those to be the facts.

Q. Mr. Wolfe, did you use any influence or make any suggestion of any kind to Lexius Henson to make you his beneficiary?

Mr. Faget: We object, may it please the Court. It's leading in the first place; second, it's a direct question upon a transaction—"did you do this". There's a transaction between him and the deceased. The transaction is dead, he can't speak, and that's a self-serving declaration.

Mr. Hood: May Your Honor please, in our opinion the will will stand or fall on the proposition of law, that where a fiduciary relation exists that the utmost good faith will have to be shown on the part of the proponent, or the one claiming an interest in the transaction, as to the benefit claimed or sought.

The Court: I think he can answer that question. I am going to let him do it.

Mr. Faget excepts.

Mr. Hood: Your Honor, please—

The Court: I have already ruled, Mr. Hood. I have given you plenty of time to argue the case; I have heard both sides now and it is time for me to rule. I am going to overrule the objection.

Mr. Hood excepts.

Q. Mr. Wolfe, did you use any influence or say anything to Lexius Henson to get him to make this will in your favor?

Mr. Faget: Now we object.

The Court: Objection overruled. That's the same question as I understand. You can answer yes or no.

A. On the contrary, Mr. Dagrall, I tried to prevail upon Henson not to make it.

SUPREME COURT

Ex Parte HUGH HENSON AND MATTIE LOU HENSON, App-llant.

Q. Just answer the question yes or no.

A. Not to make me his beneficiary.

Mr. Dagnall: Couldn't he be permitted to say that he tried to get him not to?

The Court: I don't think so.

Q. Don't say now anything that Lexius Henson told you. Don't tell the Court and Jury what Lexius Henson told you. Just answer this question:

A. I have answered it. I said, on the contrary, I tried to prevail upon him not to make me his beneficiary.

Q. What was generally the nature of your business with him?

A. Why, I represented him on three or four occasions in the Recorder's Court. He drank occasionally, and when he did he generally got in trouble. And I represented him in connection with his prospective divorce proceedings from his wife.

Q. Now, what would you advise him in reference to that divorce proceeding?

A. I told him he could not secure a divorce in South Carolina, that it would be necessary for him to leave the State.

Mr. Paget: We seriously object to all this, Your Honor.

The Court: Well, that's a different proposition. Of course, I am not going to understand your objection unless you do object.

Mr. Paget: Well, we don't want to be captious after Your Honor has ruled.

The Court: That's a different proposition than the other question. If he wants to go ahead into other matters which will involve a transaction between him and Lexius, that's a different proposition. You have got to be mighty careful about that Section there; it mighty near shuts a man's mouth.

Q. Mr. Wolfe, did you ever suggest to Henson to

SUPREME COURT 43

Ex R. M. WOLFE, as Administrator, Respondent

make some charitable institution the beneficiary?

A. I did.

Mr. Hood: We object.

The Court: Now, Mr. Dagnall, I will hear what you have got to say about that. You see, here's a transaction or communication between them. If this jury finds in his favor, and you run counter to that Section 435, your whole time is wasted because it just simply means that it comes back for another trial of the case. And that's the hardest Section to keep off of in a case of this kind I ever saw.

Gen. Bonham: I don't hesitate to say, may it please the Court, that I believe the proponent of a will has the right, even though he be a beneficiary thereunder, to testify to the execution of the will. It's an ex parte proposition, this thing of proving a will in solemn form, it isn't like a general action at law.

The Court: I believe Section 435 will cut out those things. It says, any transaction or communication.

Gen. Wolfe: Does Your Honor think that I can testify as to the manner of the execution of that will, how it came about and how it was executed?

The Court: I don't know, General; I am doubtful about that.

Gen. Bonham: Never mind about that, Mr. Wolfe.

Mr. Dagnall: We will ask Your Honor to note an exception.

The Court: Well, let's get the ruling clear so that there won't be any hereafter about what the ruling was. What was your question now?

Mr. Dagnall: What he did with reference to trying to get this man to make this will in favor of a charitable institution.

Gen. Bonham: We just want to note our exceptions to Your Honor's ruling.

The Court: All right, sir.

Gen. Bonham excepts.

SUPREME COURT

In Re: HUGH HENSON AND MATTIE LEE HENSON, Appellant.

Q. Mr. Wolfe, how old was Lexius Henson?

A. Why, I don't think, Mr. Dagnall, he was more than sixty years old.

Q. How long after his death before you learned of it?

A. Well, I left here, you know, in the early part of 1919 and went to Columbia to take up my duties as Attorney General, and I lost track of my practice here and lost track of old Henson, and I knew that I had some of his papers, his will and some other papers that belonged to him, and he had bought some clothes from me once or twice, and on one occasion, I think it had been considerable time since I heard from him, and I wrote to his employer, Goss, to ascertain from him what had become of him. Goss, as he testified, and other, didn't answer my letter, and then I wrote him again. He didn't answer that. Subsequently, I came to Anderson on one of my visits and I saw Goss on the street and asked him what had become of Henson. He told me Henson was dead.

Q. When was that?

A. That was my first information as to Henson's death.

Q. When was that?

A. And I suppose it was——

Q. When was that in reference to the time you probated the will, how long before?

A. It was the day that I probated the will.

Q. Do you remember when that was?

A. Why, it was the date of the probate, Mr. Dagnall; I have forgotten. That's in evidence, I think.

Gen. Bonham: No, it ain't in evidence.

The witness: Well, it ought to be.

Mr. Dagnall: We didn't introduce the will.

The witness: I thought you had introduced the whole record. At any rate, it was the date that I pro-

bated the will that I found out he was dead.

Q. Do you know when Henson's wife died?

A. No. The only information I received about that was in that letter there, which is not in evidence. She died some months though before he did.

Q. What, if anything, did Henson tell you relative to his wife and children having affection for him?

Mr. Paget: We object, may it please the Court.

Mr. Dagnall: It may be objectional under that Section of the Code; I don't know. It's mighty hard to know, as Your Honor says.

The Court: It's the hardest Section I have seen anywhere to construe.

Mr. Dagnall: Your Honor, if the Court is doubtful about the proposition I will withdraw it.

The Court: I think in order to render it incompetent it would have to of course refer to the transaction about which we are inquiring now; it would have to have some relation or reference to it. I mean the transaction between the deceased and the witness would have to have some relation or bearing upon the transaction that is now before the Court before it would be incompetent.

Q. Mr. Wolfe, what is that? Did you receive that letter through the mail?

A. Yes, sir, this letter came to me through the mail.

Q. Do you recognize the handwriting?

A. Yes, sir.

Mr. Dagnall: We offer this letter in evidence.

Q. Whose handwriting is it?

A. Lexius Henson's.

We offer the envelope and letter in evidence.

Envelope and letter introduced in evidence and marked exhibits C and D, respectively.

[For envelope and letter, see addenda.]

Mr. Hood: No questions.

SUPREME COURT 46

In re Will HUGH HENSON AND MATTIE LEE HENSON, Appellant.

HERMAN BAILEY, a witness for appellant, recalled, testified as follows:

RE-DIRECT EXAMINATION by Mr. Dagnall.

Q. Judge, are these papers a part of the judgment roll of your office in this case?

A. Yes, sir.

Q. This is the warrant of appraisement?

A. Yes, sir.

Q. This is the Petition to prove the will?

A. Yes, sir.

Mr. Hood: May your Honor please, we don't think those matters are competent. This is a trial de novo, and I don't know what is contained in that record he is introducing there.

Gen. Bonham: We are simply proving his appointment as administrator with the will annexed.

Mr. Hood: Well, may it please Your Honor, I don't know that any of that is competent, because the question turns on whether this is a will or not. Of course, it is admitted in common form as a matter of record, and, as a matter of fact, we are perfectly willing to admit that it was admitted in common form. If my friend will let me see the papers that he is offering it may be that I will consent to it.

Mr. Dagnall: Certainly.

Mr. Hood: Your Honor, please, I don't think it's competent to introduce this record.

The Court: What is it, the record of appointment as administrator?

Mr. Dagnall: Yes, sir. We want to show that the Court has jurisdiction, that Mr. Wolfe was acting and was duly qualified.

Gen. Bonham: This is the situation, Your Honor, please. The contestants in this case gave notice to the Judge of Probate requiring Mr. Wolfe to prove this will in solemn form, and he brought his Petition under the Statute alleging that he was the administrator with

SUPREME COURT 47

In re S. M. WOLFE, as Administrator, Respondent.

the will annexed. We are simply proving his appointment.

The Court: Go ahead, sir; the objection is overruled.

Mr. Hood excepts.

Mr. Dagnall: We offer this Petition and Qualification in evidence.

Mr. Paget: You have two there, I notice, Judge.

The witness: I think one is a copy.

The Court: Well, you are just offering the original?

Mr. Dagnall: Yes, sir.

Mr. Hood: Mr. Dagnall, does that petition show when Henson died?

Mr. Dagnall: Yes, sir; on or about the 21st day of November, 1920.

Petition to prove will, introduced in evidence and marked exhibit E; Letters Testamentary, introduced in evidence and marked exhibit F; Certificate of Appointment, introduced in evidence and marked exhibit G; Citation for Letters of Administration, introduced in evidence and marked exhibit H; Administration Bond, introduced in evidence and marked exhibit I; Warrant of Appraisement, introduced in evidence and marked exhibit J; Probate, introduced in evidence and marked exhibit K.

(Proponent rests.)

HUGH HENSON, a witness for Contestants, being duly sworn, testified as follows:

DIRECT EXAMINATION by Mr. Hood.

Q. Who was your father, Hugh?

A. Lexius Henson.

Q. Where do you live now?

A. Waynesboro.

Q. Waynesboro, Georgia?

A. Yes, sir.

Q. How far is that from Augusta?

48 SUPREME COURT

Ex Parte HIGH HENSON AND MATTIE LEE HENSON, Appellant.

A. Thirty miles.
Q. Who do you live with?
A. My grandmother.
Q. Is your grandmother with whom you live your mother's mother, or your father's mother?
A. My mother's mother.
Q. How many children did your father and mother have?

189

A. Two only.
Q. What is the name of the other?
A. Mattie Lee Henson.
Q. Where was your mother raised?
A. In Wade County, Waynesboro, Georgia.
Q. That's adjoining Richmond County?
A. Yes, sir.
Q. How long did your father and mother live in Anderson?

190

A. Lived in Anderson about ten years.
Q. Where did your father live—where did they live at the time that your mother left Anderson?
A. Out on Newel Street.
Q. That's in the City of Anderson?
A. Yes, sir.
Q. How long did they live in that house?
A. Lived in that house about eight years.
Q. Who lived there?
A. Just the family.
Q. Who composed the family—just your father and your mother and yourself and your sister?

191

A. Yes, sir.
Q. Who supported the family?
A. Lexius Henson.
Q. Your father, you mean?
A. Yes, sir.
Q. Did your father and mother live together during that time?

192

A. Yes, sir, lived pleasant together.

SUPREME COURT 49

In RE E. M. WOLFE, as Administrator, Respondent.

Q. Tell when and under what circumstances your mother left Anderson?
A. She was sick, taken sick, and he sent her home until she got well, and she went there and got sick and never was able to get back, and died there.
Q. What do you mean by "sending her home"?

193

A. She was sick and she wanted to go home to her mother... didn't have any one to take care of her and wait on her like she wanted to be.
Q. Whose home did she go to?
A. To her mother's home.
Q. Where she died?
A. Yes, sir.
Q. How long after she left here before she died?
A. It was about two months.
Q. When did she die?
A. She died in 1919—it was 1920.

194

Q. Died in 1920?
A. Yes, sir.
Q. In January, 1920?
A. Yes, sir.
Mr. Dagnall: Don't lead your witness.
Q. Who went with your mother when she left here?
A. My sister.
Q. What did you do?

195

A. I continued to stay here with my father.
Q. Did you continue to live in the same house, you and your father?
A. Yes, sir.
Q. Did your father continue to live with your mother?
A. Yes, sir.
Q. Until your mother went back to her mother's?
A. Yes, sir.
Q. Where were you when your mother died?
A. In Anderson with my father.

196

50

SUPREME COURT

Ex Parte HUGH HENSON AND MATTIE LEE HENSON, Appellant.

Q. Did you and your father go to your mother's funeral?

A. No, sir, he was real sick at the time and he couldn't go, but I went.

Q. What did you do after the funeral?

A. I came back to Anderson.

Q. Who did you live with?

A. My father.

Q. How long did you and he continue here?

A. Continued here three or four months.

Q. Well, now, go ahead and tell us what you did then and what your father did.

A. Why, I just stayed around with him and he taken care of me until he got ready to go back to Waynesboro, and after we got ready to go back to Waynesboro we packed up everything we had and left.

Q. And went where?

A. Went from here to Augusta.

Q. All right, and then where?

A. Then, from there to Waynesboro.

Q. Well, who did you go to in Waynesboro?

A. Went to his mother-in-law's, where his wife died at.

Q. Then what became of you?

A. I came back to Augusta.

Q. What became of him?

A. He come back to Augusta with me and put me in school, and I started to school, and he went back to Waynesboro again. He brought me back to Augusta, and I went to school, and so he went back to his mother's.

Q. He went back to who?

A. To his mother's.

Q. To his mother's?

A. Yes, sir—his mother-in-law's.

Q. He went back to your grandmother's?

A. Yes, sir.

SUPREME COURT

51

In re B. H. WOLFE, as Administrator, Respondent.

Q. At Waynesboro?

A. Yes, sir.

Q. Well, what became of him after that?

A. He staid down there just about two months, and then he came back to Augusta, and then came back to Anderson again.

Q. Well, go on now and tell what became of him after that?

A. And after that, about two or three months later, he came back to Augusta again, and he took sick at the time he got there, so he went to Waynesboro and told my grandmother that he come home to—

Q. You can't tell what somebody else said unless you were present. Did you hear him tell your grandmother?

Gen. Bonham: I object.

A. My sister, she heard him.

Mr. Dagnall: That would be in conflict with Section 400 of the Code, wouldn't it?

The Court: Not if he heard it. If he heard it, and he was not talking to him but to somebody else, I think he could testify to it. If he was talking to him, why he couldn't testify to it.

Q. Who was he talking to when he made that statement?

A. My sister and my grandmother.

Q. And you were present?

A. No, sir.

Q. Oh, well, if you didn't hear him make the statement you can't tell it then. What became of him then, Hugh?

A. Well, after he left Waynesboro, he come to Augusta and taken sick; taken sick right at once.

Q. Well, go on.

A. He taken sick and had pneumonia. After he staid there about two weeks, he taken sick one Monday morning and died that Thursday night.

Ex Parte HUGH HENSON AND MATTIE LEE HENSON, Appellant.

Q. Died in Augusta?
A. Yes, sir.
Q. Were you present at the time of his death?
A. Yes, sir.
Q. Did he make any statement—
Mr. Dagnall: We object, Your Honor. This is an interested party.
The Court: Yes; I don't know what the question is going to be yet, Mr. Dagnall.
Mr. Hood: May it please Your Honor, we are not wanting to bring out any conversation or any transaction of course that would be in violation of the rule. I will ask this question with a view to developing the situation, may Your Honor, please.
Q. Did you know that your father had made a will?
A. No, sir. I did not.
Q. When was the first that you knew that he had made a will?
A. Not until—
Mr. Dagnall: We object to that if that comes from his father.
The Court: Well, if he brings out anything his father said to him, why of course it would be incompetent.
Q. Did you know until after your father's death whether he had made a will or not?
A. No, sir. I did not.
Q. Did your father make any statement to you or in your presence while he was sick?
Mr. Dagnall: We object. That would be a transaction.
The Court: He can answer that yes or no, but he can't go any further unless it was as I say, unless it was a transaction or conversation to other people and not to him. If he was there taking part in the conversation in any shape or form, even though he might be

Ex Parte W. R. WOLFE, as Administrator, Respondent.

speaking to another person at the time, it wouldn't be competent, because that would be a communication made to him.
Q. Hugh, how old are you?
A. Nineteen years old.
Q. Did your father own any land?
A. Never did, sir.
Q. Where was he living in 1919?
A. 119 Newell Street.
Q. Was that the same house that he had been living in for the past eight years?
A. Yes, sir.
Q. Did he have any other place rented?
A. No, sir.
Q. Did anybody else live in the house besides his family, his wife and children?
A. No, sir.
CROSS-EXAMINATION by Mr. Dagnall.
Q. Where was your father living in April, 1913?
A. On McDuffie Street.
Q. City of Anderson?
A. Yes, sir.
Q. Why, your mother died in 1919, didn't she?
A. 1920, sir.
Q. Well, you heard me read this letter here yesterday, didn't you?
A. Yes, sir.
Q. From your father to Mr. Wolfe?
A. Yes, sir.
Q. Where he says she died in January last year, 1919?
A. No, sir, she died January 1920.
Q. Your father was mistaken then, was he?
A. Yes, sir.
MATTIE LEE HENSON, a witness for Contestants, being duly sworn, testified as follows:
DIRECT EXAMINATION by Mr. Hood.

54

SUPREME COURT

Ex Parte HUGH BENSON AND MATTIE LEE BENSON, Appellant.

Q. Mattie Lee, where do you live?
A. Waynesboro.
Q. What State?
A. Waynesboro, Georgia.
Q. Who do you live with?
A. With my grandmother.
Q. Was that your father's mother, or your mother's mother?
A. My mother's mother.
Q. How long have you lived with your grandmother?
A. Ever since my mother died, when she left Anderson and went down there.
Q. Do you remember when she left Anderson?
A. No, sir.
Q. How old are you?
A. Twelve.
Q. You are twelve years old?
A. Yes, sir.
Q. Who went to Georgia with your mother when she went there?
A. Not any one, just me and her.
Q. Just you?
A. And her, yes, sir.
Q. Why did your mother go to Georgia?
A. She was sick and didn't have any one to wait on her.
Q. Where had she lived up to the time that she went?
A. Out at Mr. Tucker's house on McDuffie Street.
Q. Who lived there?
A. My mother and my father and me and my brother.
Q. And your father is Losius P. Henson?
A. Yes, sir.
Q. Who supported the family, Mattie Lee?
A. My father.

213

214

215

216

55

SUPREME COURT

Ex Parte H. M. WOLFE, as Administrator, Respondent.

Q. How long did he support the family?
A. As long as we was there.
Q. As long as you were there?
A. Yes, sir.
Q. Did he contribute to the support of yourself and your mother after you went to Waynesboro?
A. Yes, sir.
Q. Did your father live with your mother up till the time she left Anderson?
A. Yes, sir.
Q. When was the last time you saw your father before leaving Anderson?
A. Why, he come down to Waynesboro.
Q. Well, I said now before you left Anderson, before you and your mother left Anderson?
A. Before we left?
Q. Yes, before you left Anderson, where did you last see your father at?
A. In August.
Q. No, before you left Anderson?
A. Oh, down at the depot.
Q. Did he go to the depot with you and your mother?
A. Yes, sir.
Q. Do you remember when your mother died?
A. Yes, sir.
Q. When was it?
A. January 1920.
Q. She died in January, 1920?
A. Yes, sir, on Thursday.
Q. Do you remember when your father died?
A. He died November, 1920.
Q. Did you see your father after you and your mother left Anderson?
A. He come down to Waynesboro. He was down there for the Christmas, but he died before Christmas come.

217

218

219

220

56

SUPREME COURT

Ex Parte RUSH HENSON AND MATTIE LEE HENSON, Appellant.

Q. He came down to?
A. Waynesboro.
Q. Who did he come to see?
A. He come to see me and my grandmother and us.
Q. Where did he stay while he was there?
A. He staid down at our house.
Q. Staid down at your grandmother's house?
A. Yes, sir.

Mr. Dagnall: No questions.

PARIS R. PRYOR, a witness for the contestants, being duly sworn, testified as follows:

DIRECT EXAMINATION by Mr. Hood.

Q. Paris, where do you live?
A. I live in the City of Augusta.
Q. What relation if any were you to Lexius P. Henson's wife and to Lexius Henson?
A. Why, Lexius Henson's wife was my sister.
Q. So, therefore, was your brother-in-law?
A. Brother-in-law, yes, sir.
Q. These children here is your niece and nephew.
A. Yes, sir, my niece and nephew, those little children.
Q. Where does your mother live?
A. My mother lives in Waynesboro.
Q. Where do these children live at Waynesboro?
A. These children lives at Waynesboro. The little girl stays at Waynesboro, and the boy staid with me while he was going to school at Augusta.
Q. Paris, were you present when Lexius died?
A. Yes, sir, I was there.
Q. Did you hear Lexius make any statement to his son, Hugh?
A. Yes, sir, I did.

Mr. Dagnall: Your Honor, I would like to ask the witness a question or two so I can object to this. We think it incompetent to go into the conversation. I

57

SUPREME COURT

Ex Parte S. M. WOLFE, as Administrator, Respondent.

would like to cross-examine the witness in order to show his interest.

The Court: Why, I don't know that it is necessary for you to do that just at this time.

Mr. Dagnall: He is asking the question now as to what he heard Lexius say. What I want to show is, that this man was appointed administrator in Augusta and that he drew out the money, and that he would therefore be an interested party.

Mr. Hood: We will admit. Your Honor, please, that he was appointed administrator under the laws of Georgia of this estate, and that he drew out the seventeen hundred and odd dollars in the Bank of Anderson to the credit of Lexius Henson.

Mr. Dagnall: I want to show that this was an interested witness.

Gen. Ionham: He was the administrator, and he was under the Section of the Code.

Mr. Farst: I can get Your Honor an authority on that. I have an authority on that.

The Court: Well I would like to hear it.

The Court: I will let you examine him, Mr. Dagnall and see whether or not he is interested. That's the only way to find out.

EXAMINATION by Mr. Dagnall.

Q. You are an undertaker, I believe, in Augusta?
A. I beg pardon. I am not an undertaker, I am an insurance man.
Q. Lexius Henson owed you something, didn't he?
A. Owed me?
Q. Yes, for funeral expenses and doctors bills?
A. Well, it had to be done. Of course, there wasn't anybody to look up to it but me to bury him. If I got it, it was all right, and if I didn't get it, it was all right.
Q. You paid all the expenses of the funeral?
A. Why, yes, sir, I paid all expenses.

Q. How much did the estate owe you?

A. The estate owed me, I think, after his funeral altogether somewhere along about three hundred and fifty dollars. They walked him up, and all like that, and buying clothes.

Gen. Bonham: I think, may it please the Court, under that showing he is not entitled to testify.

A. I beg pardon, I wasn't interested, but it was just as my duty. There wasn't anybody to bury him but me; I had to do it.

Mr. Hood: Now if Your Honor, please, if he did, he would be entitled to recover for those funeral expenses against the will or under the administration in Georgia. It's a legal liability that is imposed on the estate, as I see it. And whether the will is sustained or not, he is entitled to be reimbursed out of the administration funds through his appointment as administrator in Georgia, or out of the funds that may be derived by the administrator with the will annexed here in South Carolina, if the will should be upheld.

The Court: The only question Mr. Hood—we are not trying that point—is as to whether or not he is an interested party and whether or not he would be debarred from testifying to any communication or transaction between he and Lexius Henson. Now, gentlemen, is it your contention that if this man is a creditor, that is, if the estate owes him his expenses for his had illness or for his funeral expenses, burial expenses, that that interest as a creditor of the estate would disqualify him from testifying?

Gen. Bonham: Yes, sir.

The Court: I don't think so under this Section.

Gen Bonham excepts.

The Court: The law requires that to be paid, it don't make any difference what sort of disposition Lexius Henson tried to make of his property. It's got

to be just before it can be generous; that's the law.

Q. What statement, then, did you hear Lexius Henson make to his son Hugh Henson?

A. He said—this is the truth—he told his boy—he handed him the book, the bank book—

Q. Have you got that?

A. He has got it there.

Q. Look at that and see if that is the book?

A. Yes, sir. He handed this bank book to him and told him that he wanted him and his little daughter to have everything that he possessed. Now that's the truth and nothing but the truth, so help me God. That's what he said.

Q. Paris, who else was present when he died?

A. Well, there was the presence of an old lady in the house, my oldest sister Mary. She is in Augusta.

Q. Did you know that he had made a will at that time?

A. I did not.

Q. When did you first know that he had made a will?

A. I didn't know anything about that he had made a will until some—I think Mr. Wolfe written me that he held a claim, had a will. And this is the second letter—

Q. No, I am not asking you about that letter.

Mr. Hood: May it please Your Honor, I would like to introduce that book in evidence there. And this is the Bank of Anderson, Anderson, S. C., and it is the usual deposit book.

Q. You were appointed administrator of the estate in Georgia, were you, Paris?

A. Yes, sir.

Q. How did you know that he had made seventeen or eighteen hundred dollars in the Bank of Anderson?

A. Well, how I come by it—

Q. I didn't ask you how you came by it, I asked you

SUPREME COURT

In re: HUGH HENSON AND BATTE LEE HENSON, Appellee.

how you knew as administrator, under appointment in Georgia, that he had seventeen hundred and fifty dollars and fifty cents in the Bank of Anderson?

A. Well, he gave me the book.

Q. You got it from that book?

A. Yes, sir.

Bank deposit book introduced in evidence and marked exhibit (K).

Gen. Benham: We object to this testimony on the same ground. I want my objection entered now. I understand Your Honor has overruled our contention. Here is a direct transaction between this man and the deceased in relation to this very estate. I will ask Your Honor to allow us to note our objection.

The Court: All right, sir. The only interest he has is as a creditor. The expenses of his death and burial have got to be paid, anyhow, it don't make any difference what the will is, if he left a sufficient estate to pay it; therefore, I don't think his interest in it can be affected by the event of this action one way or the other.

Gen. Benham excepts.

Gen. Barham: Come down.

(Contestants close.)

The Court: Gentlemen, I am going to have to direct a verdict in this case: I don't think there is anything here to leave to you. If there was, I certainly would be glad to shift the responsibility off to you. It seems to me the evidence here is practically all one way. This paper that is offered in evidence in my judgment is unquestionably the will of this man that it purports to be. Now it is not for you and it is not for me to make a will for a man. If a man wants to give his property away to somebody else besides his children, he has got a right to do it, and we can't make wills for people in a Court, neither a jury nor a Judge. All we can do is to say whether or not the paper which

---

In re: M. WOLFE, as Administrator, Respondent.

is offered in evidence is the last will and testament of the person whose will it purports to be. Now all the evidence, it seems to me, that has been offered here goes to show, beyond any question in my mind, that this was the last will and testament, that it represented his wishes. There is no evidence, as I construe it, against that view of it. If a man wants to cut his children out, he has got a right to do that; there is no law against it. We may not approve of it, you and I may think that was the wrong thing for this man to do, that we wouldn't do a thing of that sort; nevertheless, if he wanted to do it, he had the right to do it, and it isn't for you and it isn't for me, sitting here as the Court, to deny him that right; we can't do it lawfully.

And, no matter which view we might take of this case, whether or not after the will has been proven that it was not excepted to, and then upon the other side to show that it was burden is then upon the other side to show that it was not brought in good faith, or whether the burden is on the other party in this case, that is, on Mr. Wolfe, to show that the whole transaction was free from any undue influence brought to bear on this man—in either case I think the evidence fully justifies the Court and requires me to direct a verdict in this case, for you to find that this is the true last will and testament of Lewis Henson. As I say, you may not have done a thing of that sort, you may not have cut your children out. I may be that I disapprove of a thing of that kind. And I do, unless there is mighty good cause for it. But, nevertheless, it is a right of a man and it is not for you to say that he shan't do it if he wants to do it. Where he has property, if he doesn't want to give it to his children he don't have it to do, and you can't force him to do it and I can't force him to do it. All we are called upon to pass on here is whether or not this paper which has been offered in evidence here is the

Ex Parte HUGH HENSON AND MATTIE LEE HENSON, Appellant.

true last will and testament of Lexius Henson. And it seems to me that all the evidence is one way. And even if there is a presumption that isn't the right thing to do for a lawyer to draw a will for his client, or for the client to draw a will in favor of the lawyer, I say even if there is a presumption that it is undue influence, and that's the contention of the other side, will it seems to me that the undisputed evidence here completely wipes out any presumption of that kind.

Now I have listened attentively to the lawyers, I have given them plenty of time to argue as long as they wanted to. I haven't shut any of them off. I have heard all the authorities and I followed the testimony very close, and that's my conclusion in the case, gentlemen. If I am wrong, why there is a higher Court to correct the verdict. But I feel that I am right, and, feeling that way, it doesn't make any difference to this Court what becomes of it hereafter. All I can do in any case—and I intend to do that just as long as I sit on the Bench—is to do just what I think is the right thing to do in a case, no matter who it hurts and no matter who it favors. And, feeling that way about it, gentlemen, why I will have to direct a verdict in this case that you answer these questions here in favor of the proponent of the will.

Now, Mr. Foreman, you take this paper and write "Yes" to these three questions here and sign your name as foreman.

ORDER DECEMBER 13, 1923.

The above matter was an appeal from the Probate Court of Anderson County, was tried by me with a jury on the 12th day of December, 1923. This was a proceeding to prove in solemn form the will of Lexius P. Henson. The following issues were submitted to the jury under the direction of the Court:

(1) Was the paper propounded as the last Will and Testament of Lexius P. Henson duly and legally

In Re E. M. WOLFE, et Administrator, Respondent.

executed?

(2) When said paper was executed, did Lexius P. Henson have Testamentary Capacity?

(3) Is the paper propounded, the true, last will and testament of Lexius P. Henson?

The jury under the direction of the Court having decided all the issues in the affirmative, it is ORDERED AND DECREED, That the paper propounded as the last will and testament of Lexius P. Henson, deceased be, and the same is hereby declared and adjudged to be the last will and testament of the said Lexius P. Henson, and that the said will is hereby adjudged and decreed to be proven in due form of law. Signed H. F. Rice, Judge Presiding in Tenth Judicial Circuit, December 13, 1923.

EXCEPTIONS.

1. Error in refusing to submit to the jury the issue proposed by contestants, namely, "Did Lexius P. Henson reside in, or was he an inhabitant of, the County of Anderson, or the State of South Carolina, at the time of his death?"

2. Error in permitting the Proponent of the will to answer the questions as to whether or not the will was in his handwriting, as to whether he wrote the typewritten parts, whether he wrote any other part of it, and as to who wrote it, the error being in permitting the Proponent of the will to testify as to a transaction or communication between himself and the deceased, he being the sole beneficiary under the will.

3. Error in permitting the Proponent to answer the following: "Did you use any influence or say anything to Lexius P. Henson to get him to make this will in your favor?" the error being that it related to a transaction or communication with the deceased in regard to the making of the will, in which Proponent was sole beneficiary, and was a leading question and called for an expression of opinion only.

SUPREME COURT

Ex Parte HUGH HENSON AND MATTIE LEE HENSON, Appellant.

4. Error in permitting the Proponent of the will to answer the question, "Mr. Wolfe, did you ever suggest to Henson to make some charitable institution the beneficiary?", the error being that the answer related to a communication or transaction between the two relating to the will, under which Proponent is sole beneficiary.

5. Error in directing a verdict in favor of Proponent on all issues submitted, the error being in holding that there was no testimony to go to the jury on the issues submitted by the Court.

Addenda: Exhibits C and D

Envelope: "After 5 days Return to L. Henson Box 41, Anderson, S. C." Post Marked: "Anderson, S. C. Jul. 20, 1920 8-30 A." Addressed: "Mr. S. M. Wolfe Attorney-General, Columbia, S. C."

Written on one of S. W. Williford's Bill Heads

Letter: Anderson, S. C., 7-19-20

Mr. S. M. Wolfe, Columbia S. C.
Dear Kind friend. it has been a long time since Ive seen you it must been almost 2 years since I saw you last. I lost my wife last year in January 1919 over year ago. I sent her home in Georgia 1918 in November. I sent her there for good and she took sick 2 months afterwards. something like that.

Mr. Wolfe I want to know if you had any good suit of clause you want to sell. I want some good looking suit if you have them I am wearing the same suit of close I bought from you 2 years a go Write me and let me know what you have . . . (Word mutilated) . . I do not want any suit with hole in them and also I do not want coat with strap back and none split way up in the back I do not want them I want them like the style you sold me I know that you are a great sport some like myself. I am an all round sport let me know what color and also price and have you got that same over coat you show me once at the house. let me heare from you by return mail if you have the time

I am yours For Good Clothing
L. Henson
Anderson, S. C.

P. O. Box 41

State of South Carolina
Anderson County
....
* Last Will and Testament
Lexius P. Henson.

I, Lexius P. Henson, at present of City of Anderson, in the County and State above named, being of sound and disposing mind, and of Ordinary bodily health, and absolutely without inducement, or any suggestion of influence on the part of the beneficiary herein, do now make and declare this to be my last solemn will and testament to wit; that in the event of my dying a "grass widower," a widower, or married to my present wife Hattie Henson, I will and bequeath to my friend and attorney Samuel M. Wolfe my entire estate consisting of Life Insurance under policy in the Metropolitan Life Insurance Co, and under the policy in the Life and Casualty Insurance Company of Tennessee, and all other personalty or realty whatsoever, for his sole and absolute property! my wife and children being without affection for me and my wife being undutiful, perverse and a source of constant annoyance and disturbance, and there being no one else except a brother whose where about I do not know and any lawyer aforesaid being my preference and the one I feel most attachment for.

Witness my hand and seal this 30th of April - A.D. 1918

Lexius P. Henson [Seal]

The foregoing instrument was subscribed, sealed published and declared by Lexius P. Henson as and for his last will and testament in our presence and in the presence of each of us, and we, at his request, at the same time, in his presence, and in the presence of each of us, hereunto subscribed our names as attesting witnesses thereto, and to the fact that in our opinion, testator is of apparently sound and disposing mind.

This 30 th. April, 1918.

Made in the USA
Middletown, DE
22 March 2019